NATURE LOVER'S BOOK
NUMBER 2

Country Walks with Uncle Merry

ENID BLYTON'S

NATURE LOVER'S BOOK NUMBER 2

Country Walks with Uncle Merry

Armada

First published in the U.K. in 1944 by
Evans Brothers Limited. This edition
was first published in 1971 by
Wm. Collins Sons & Co Ltd., 14 St. James's Place,
London S.W.1.

© Enid Blyton 1944

Printed in Great Britain by
Love & Malcomson Ltd.,
Brighton Road, Redhill, Surrey.

CHAPTER 1

THE FOUR RAMBLERS

It was a cold winter's day at the beginning of January. In the village of Greenwoods the smoke rose up from every cottage in straight spires of blue.

Round one big fire, in a cosy little play-room, sat three children. One was a big boy of eleven, frowning over a book about aeroplanes. Next to him was his sister, a little younger, but so like him that everyone took them for twins. The third was a small boy of about six, chalking in a book, his tongue out as he worked.

"I wish it would snow or something," said Pat. "I hate this nasty, cold, shivery weather. Nothing to do out-of-doors. Nothing to see. Nothing to hear. I wish it was summer-time."

There came the click of a garden-gate. The children jumped up to see who was coming. "It's the man who has come to live next door," said Pat. "You know, the man who writes books. He looks rather nice, I think—not a bit learned or fierce. I wonder what he writes books about."

The children forgot about him after a while. They were bored with staying indoors so long. They would not go out because they said there was nothing to do out-of-doors, and nothing to see. Very soon they began to quarrel.

Pat upset John's chalks. There they lay, all over the floor. "You clumsy thing!" cried John. "Now you've broken all the points!"

"I haven't," said Pat. "You never do have sharp points."

Janet took her little brother's side. "Help John pick up his chalks!" she said. "You're unkind!"

"Don't talk to me like that!" said Pat, and he gave Janet such a push that she fell over on top of John. He went down on the floor with a crash, and began to howl loudly:

"I've hurt my arm, I've hurt my arm! It's broken, it's broken!"

The crash and yells were heard downstairs and Mrs. Thomson came running up the stairs to see what the matter was. Behind her came the man from next door. John's yells stopped as soon as the two grown-ups came into the room.

"Just a quarrel," said the man from next door. "Well, what can you expect with three children cooped up round the fire on a lovely day like this, when they ought to be out-of-doors?"

"I'd like them to go out," said Mrs. Thomson, "but they make such a fuss when I suggest it."

"It's no good going out in January," said Pat, rather sulkily. "There's nothing to be seen, no matter where we go. It's different in the spring and summer."

"Well," said the man from next door, "I'm going out for a walk this afternoon—and I have a feeling I shall see quite a lot—animals, birds, trees, even flowers, perhaps!"

The children stared at him. "But it's only just past

6

Christmas," said John. "It's the middle of winter. There's nothing exciting to be found at all."

"You're quite wrong!" said the man. "Come with me this afternoon, and I'll show you how wrong you are. My name is Peter Meredith. I write books about birds, but there isn't anything I don't love about the country—except perhaps rats. Well," said Mr. Meredith, turning to go, "be at my front gate at half-past two sharp, will you? And we'll go off for a walk and see what we can find on this bitter-cold but sunny day of mid-winter."

At twenty-seven minutes past two Pat, Janet, and John were outside the front gate next door. A minute later out came Mr. Meredith—and with him was someone else!

It was a small black Scottie dog, scampering along on short black legs, his tail waving like a black plume in the air. The children stared at him in delight.

"Is he yours?" asked John. "Oh, I do like him!"

"Let me introduce you to Fergus, the best and the most sporting little dog in the world," said Mr. Meredith. "Shake paws, Fergus."

Fergus held up a front paw, and the three children each shook it solemnly. Then Fergus hung out his pink tongue, panted hard as if he had been running, and jumped round Mr. Meredith excitedly.

"Yes—we're off for a walk," said Mr. Meredith. The children beamed.

"Is Fergus coming too?" said John.

"Of course," said Mr. Meredith. "Well—off we go! We'll go down the lane and across the fields, shall we?"

7

Fergus seemed to understand, for he set off in front of everyone on his sturdy legs.

"Everything is so bare and bleak," said Pat. "No leaves on the trees—except on the dark evergreens—the frost over everything—no birds, no animals, no insects. I hate the winter."

"Only because you don't use your eyes and ears," said Mr. Meredith, with a laugh. "Look at Fergus now —he's after some animal, isn't he?"

Fergus uttered a sharp yelp, disappeared through the hedge, and scampered out in the middle of the field. A grey form showed up for a moment, glided swiftly across the field and disappeared.

"A hare," said Mr. Meredith. "And there goes a rabbit—two of them! Look—they have been nibbling the bark from the stems of this big clump of ivy."

The children stared at the nibbled white ivy-stems. "Are the rabbits so hungry then?" asked Pat.

"Very," said Mr. Meredith. "Last week the snow was deep over these fields, and the rabbits could not get at the grass—so they nibbled the bark for food. Look—there's the rabbit's enemy. Keep still!"

The children stood quiet as mice, watching a small animal running in a snake-like manner through the hedge. For one moment it turned and stared at the children with sharp, gleaming eyes.

"A weasel," said Mr. Meredith, "hunting for rats, mice, or rabbits. Many animals have difficulty these cold winter days in finding their dinners."

"I thought most animals slept all through the winter," said John, surprised.

"A good many do," said Mr. Meredith. "All around us are sleeping creatures, though we can't see them.

8

There are frogs sleeping in that frozen pond over there—bumble bees in holes in that bank—bats in hollow trees—hedgehogs in leaf-lined holes—snakes curled up together in their hiding-places. But the rabbit, the hare, the weasel, and the stoat are wideawake. So is the red fox. I saw his tracks in the snow last week up on that hill over there."

"I've never seen a wild fox," said Pat. "I wish I could. Oh, look—there goes another rabbit—and there goes Fergus!"

"Look at the bunny's white tail, bobbing up and down!" cried John. "He's gone into his hole!"

"His white bob-tail is a very good signal to the other rabbits around," said Mr. Meredith. "It catches their eye—and they know what it means at once— DANGER! So off they all go when they see somebody's white tail bobbing."

A robin hopped near to the children, and they saw his lovely red breast. His big black eyes looked at them in a very friendly manner. Then two or three sparrows flew down nearby, squabbling over a bit of bread that one of them carried in his beak.

"Look at those sparrows," said Mr. Meredith. "Do you see that the little cock-sparrows are already growing black bibs under their chins?"

"Yes—two of them have black bibs and the third hasn't," said Janet. "Is that how you can tell the cock-sparrows from the hen-sparrows? I never knew that before. Oh—they're afraid of us—they've all flown off!"

"Yes—and now the friendly, tame little robin has his chance," said Mr. Meredith.

By now the little company had gone right across the

9

fields, and were in a sheltered patch, where a small copse of trees stood. Janet stopped and pulled down a twig from a small tree.

"Look—catkins already!" she said. "Can we take some home? I like lambs' tails."

"Yes—we'll put some twigs of hazel catkins in water, and watch the tails lengthen and become full of yellow pollen," said Mr. Meredith. "That will be fun."

"Do the nuts grow from the catkins?" said John.

Mr. Meredith laughed.

"Oh no! These catkins are just tails of stamens full of pollen. The wind blows away the pollen when it is ripe and powdery—and some of it falls on to the little red seed-bearing flowers, which we will find later on, growing along the twig, looking very like leaf-buds. The nuts grow from those. There—that's a nice little bunch of catkins you've picked, Janet. They will look lovely in a vase."

"I'd like to take something home too," said John at once. "Can I pick some primroses?" The other children laughed.

"Isn't he a baby?" said Janet scornfully. "As if we could find primroses or any other flowers in cold January!"

"Well, I did see a flower just now," said John unexpectedly.

"You didn't," said Janet.

"I did!" said John.

He ran back a little way and bent down. He came back with a tiny white flower, minute and starry.

"Good boy!" said Mr. Meredith. "I saw that too, and wondered if anyone else would see it. It's chickweed. You can find it nearly all the year round. And look—there's another flower—groundsel."

"Oh, our canary likes that," said Janet, and went to pick some. "I always think the flowers look like tiny shaving brushes, Mr. Meredith."

"So they do!" said Mr. Meredith. "Now I can see two more flowers ahead of us, but I shan't show you them. You must spot them yourselves. I don't think you two elder ones are very good at seeing things—not nearly as good as young John here."

Janet and Pat looked down at the ground sharply. They must, they simply *must* find those flowers before John did. But John danced ahead, and pointed them out gleefully. "Nettles, nettles! Pink and white!"

"Will they sting?" said Janet.

"Of course not," said Mr. Meredith. "Can't you tell the difference between the stinging-nettles and the dead-nettles that never sting? Well, really, for a country child you know very little!"

He picked a piece of red dead-nettle and a piece of white. "Now, look," said Mr. Meredith, "these are both dead-nettles and cannot sting, though their leaves do look a little like those of the stinging-nettle. And look at their stalks."

The children looked and felt. "They are square—how funny!" said Pat.

"Yes," said Mr. Meredith, "that is one way you can tell a member of the dead-nettle family—by the square stem. And look at the shape of the flower—it is divided into two lips, the upper one large, and the lower one small. We call the family the Lip Family, or Labiate Family, and to it belong a great number of valuable

11

plants. I don't believe there is one single member of the large Lip Family that is harmful."

"Does the lavender belong to it?" said John. "And the wild thyme? I remember their flowers—they've got lips too."

"Quite right," said Mr. Meredith, patting him on the back. "Here is a child who really uses his eyes!"

"Do flowers all belong to different families?" asked John. "I say—wouldn't it be fun to try and find what families they all belong to!"

"Great fun," said Mr. Meredith. "Trees belong to different families too—so do birds—so do butterflies and moths—crabs and shrimps—everything! And each family has its own special ways and characters. I will show you my big flower-book one day. It is divided up into many flower families, and we have to look up each flower under the name of its own family."

"Here's another flower!" cried Pat, who had been longing to find one. "It's white, with four petals—like a white cross."

"It's the shepherd's purse," said Mr. Meredith. "Now you can tell that this flower doesn't belong to the Lip Family. It belongs to the Cross Family, the Cruciferae as we call it. All the members of this family have their petals in fours, arranged opposite one another, like a cross."

"Like the wall-flower," said Janet at once.

Mr. Meredith nodded. "Good girl! Yes—the wall-flower is one of the Cross Family. But can you tell me why this little flower has such a funny name? Shepherd's purse—why should it be called that?"

The three children stared at the plant that Mr. Mere-

12

dith held. Fergus stood up on his hind legs and tried to look at it too. It was a queer little plant, with tiny white cross-shaped flowers, and below them, growing down the stem, were funny little heart-shaped seed-boxes.

Janet stared at the seed-boxes. "I believe it's because of those," she said. "They look like tiny purses, don't they?"

"And inside is the money!" laughed Mr. Meredith, splitting a green seed-box open, and showing the little round green seeds inside. "Yes—and the name comes from the purse-shaped seed-vessels. I often wonder who named our common flowers—they have such good names, and some of them have really lovely names—like ladies' smock and old man's beard, and crane's bill."

"Let's go into the woods," said Pat, as they walked on again. "We might find something exciting there."

Mr. Meredith looked at his watch.

"Good gracious! Have you any idea what the time is? It is almost four o'clock! Let's go for a walk round your garden now," said Mr. Meredith

The three children stared at him in surprise. A walk round the garden? There wouldn't be much to see.

John said so. "There's nothing to see in the garden," he said. "It wouldn't be any fun."

"I never knew such blind children!" said Mr. Meredith. "Still, Fergus and I are very pleased to know you. We feel as if we have found two nephews and a niece, which is really very nice."

"Well, if we're two nephews and a niece, then you must be an uncle," said John seriously. "I should like you for an uncle. We already have an uncle who takes

13

us to the Zoo, and another one who sometimes takes us to the seaside. You could be the uncle that takes us for walks."

"So I could," agreed Mr. Meredith, with a twinkle.

"I shall call you Uncle Merry," said John. "That's a nice name for you—short for Meredith, you see. Uncle Merry!"

The others laughed. John was so funny—but he did have some good ideas.

Soon they arrived at their garden.

"Oh dear—how nasty and bare the garden looks! Uncle Merry, I shall think you're very clever indeed if you find lots of interesting things here," said Janet.

"Well, Janet, we'll have to hunt about a bit for some of them, but most boys and girls like doing a spot of hunting," said Uncle Merry. "But, first—just look at those flowers!"

The children stared down at a little sheltered bed that ran alongside the south wall of the house. In it was a row of quaint little yellow flowers, each with a pretty green frill just under their yellow cups.

"Buttercups," said Pat.

"Celandines," said Janet, feeling clever.

John said nothing. He knew they were neither, but he did not ever remember hearing the name.

Uncle Merry gave such a deep and hollow groan that Fergus bounded up to him in alarm. "It's all right, Fergus," said Uncle Merry. "I couldn't help groaning at these children, that's all. Buttercups and celandines! Oh, my goodness, don't either of you know what they look like and when they flower? These early January blossoms are aconites. Aconites!"

"Oh," said Janet and Pat, looking down at them. "Aconites. Aren't they pretty?"

"They are the earliest flowers of the year," said Uncle Merry, "though the winter jasmine runs it very close. Look, there's some out on the wall over there. See its starry yellow flowers."

The children saw that part of the south wall was covered with a thickly growing plant whose flowers burst out from green stems that bore no leaves. Janet thought it was lovely. She picked a few sprays. "They will look sweet in the play-room," she said. "How funny that I've never noticed this winter jasmine before."

"Well, now, what about you three going off by yourselves for a few minutes to see if you can find any other flowers," said Uncle Merry. "Go along—and I back John to find the most!"

"It's like playing hunt-the-thimble," said John, "only it's hunt-the-flower instead!"

The children separated and went different ways round their big garden. Soon they came back, and each of them had something to show Uncle Merry.

"What's this?" asked Janet, putting a spray of flowers into her friend's hand. "It grew on that dark green bush over there. It must be an evergreen, Uncle Merry, because I know the bush is green all through the winter."

All of them looked at the small starry flowers, a lovely pink in the bud, and a very pale pinkish-white when open.

"It's laurestinus," said Uncle Merry. "Can you remember that? Laurestinus, a flower that chooses to blossom very early in the year, sometimes even in December!"

"Laurestinus," repeated the children. Janet put it with her jasmine. Then Pat held out what he had found. It was a stiff waxen-looking flower, on a fat, pinky-green stalk, and the flower had many bright yellow stamens in the centre.

"It hadn't any leaves," said Pat. "I looked. What is it, Uncle Merry? It looks a bit like an anemone, only white and stiff."

"It's a Christmas rose," said Uncle Merry. "You can guess why it has that name—because it comes out at Christmas-time. It isn't in the least like a rose, and it doesn't belong to the Rose Family—Rosaceae—so you mustn't think it does. Its big leaves grow up in the spring. We will look for them then."

"There were three or four more Christmas roses out," said Pat. "It's a funny time of year to choose to come out, isn't it, Uncle Merry—in cold January?"

"It is," said Uncle Merry. "Hello—look what our friend John has found! A dandelion—and a daisy! Well, well, well, trust John to find something peculiar!"

"I know they're not really January flowers," said John, holding out the yellow dandelion and the pink-tipped daisy. "But it was so nice to see them flowering in the yellow sunshine. I think the dandelion is a lovely flower, Uncle Merry. The others always laugh at me because they say it's a horrid common weed."

"It certainly is a common weed," said Uncle Merry, "but it isn't horrid, though gardeners and farmers detest it. The flower is really lovely—at least, the flower-*head*! One dandelion head contains scores of flowers, John! If we pulled it to pieces we should find that it

16

was made up of very many tiny flowers or florets. Look—I'll pull just one out—here it is. It is complete with stamens and pistil!"

"Does it belong to any flower family we already know?" asked Janet, looking wise. "It's not the Lip Family nor the Cross Family."

"It belongs to the Composite Family," said Uncle Merry, "the Compositae. You see, the flower head is *composed* of many tiny flowers, making it a *composite* flower."

"Like the chrysanthemum," said Pat, feeling clever, "and the daisy."

"And the aster," said John, "and the marguerite and marigold."

"Quite right," said Uncle Merry. "Look—what are those things there on the grass?"

The children looked—and they looked. Janet could see only the dull green grass, set with a few weeds. John saw one or two dead leaves as well. It was Pat who suddenly guessed what Uncle Merry meant.

"Oh, I know—the worm-holes!" he said. "What a lot there are, Uncle Merry!"

They all went to have a look at them.

"They are all stuffed up," said John, puzzled. "Who stuffed up the worm-holes? Look—here's one stopped up with two dead leaves, and some bits of straw. Who could have stuffed up the holes like that?"

"The worms themselves did," said Uncle Merry. "They like to keep out the cold and the frost, so they come out at night and wriggle about to find some good things to use as stuffing. They twist their bodies round them, and then pull leaves, or stalks, or straw—whatever they have found—to their holes. They pull them

17

in, one after another—and by the morning their hole is well and truly stopped up."

"I never knew that worms were so clever," said Pat, in amazement. "I *would* like to see them doing that."

"Well, come out on a moonlight night, stand very quietly at the edge of the lawn, and watch," said Uncle Merry.

"Could I un-stuff a hole?" asked John. "Just to see what the worm has used?"

"Yes, if you like," said Uncle Merry. "The worm will have to work hard again to-night to stuff it up—but it won't mind."

John pulled out some creeper stalks—three decaying leaves—and some wisps of straw. He rubbed away a little mound of earth thrown up by the worm, very light and powdery—and then was able to see the entrance of the worm's home.

"It lives down there, in a room at the end of its long tunnel," said Uncle Merry. "It curls itself up there, and waits for night-time to come, when it wriggles out on to your lawn. It hurries home again when it fears that the birds are about."

"I've often seen a bird looking and listening for a worm on the lawn," said Janet. "It stands quite still with its head on one side, just as if it's listening for a movement below in the hole. Then it may pounce quickly and drag up a wriggling worm."

"You do use your eyes sometimes then!" said Uncle Merry, with a laugh. "Look at all the worm-casts on this lawn. Think what thousands of millions of worms there are over the countryside, working away underground, making long tunnels that help to air and drain the soil. The worms are like little ploughmen. See the fine powdery soil of this worm-cast, and think what help it is to the farmer to have so much of his soil made fine like this year after year."

"What else can we see?" asked John, looking round. Uncle Merry took them to an old wall, beneath which there was a rockery. He moved one or two stones, looking underneath. Then he found what he was looking for.

"Look," he said, "what are these?"

The children bent forward.

"Snails," said Pat. "I often wondered where they went to in the winter. What a lot of them—some are on top of others, Uncle Merry. Let me take one off. Oh--it's glued on! How funny!"

Everyone stared at the cluster of still snail-shells. Uncle Merry broke one shell away from another, and turned it upside down to show the children.

"Snails don't like the cold frosty weather," he said. "They can't find their tender green food in the winter, and so they think it would be best to sleep cold days away. It's a good idea, isn't it—better than starving!"

"Uncle Merry, the snail is all hard underneath, instead of soft," said John, tapping it with his finger. "Last summer I picked up a snail, and it was soft under here, and slimy."

"Yes—but when winter comes the snail grows a hard front door over the entrance to his shell," said Uncle Merry. "He leaves a tiny breathing-hole for himself, of course. He goes off to some sheltered place like this, and either alone or with his friends, as you see, he settles himself to sleep away the cold weather. He will stay here until the warm spring comes—then he will dissolve his hard front door and crawl away to find food, putting out his horned head to see his way."

"I'd like to take some snails into the play-room," said John. "I'll put them in a box of earth. They shall be my pets. Oh, Uncle Merry, we've found a lot of things, haven't we? I think I shall keep a sort of chart, and write down each time what we find."

"Good idea," said Uncle Merry. "You must put

THE CHAFFINCH

some birds on it though—look, do you know what bird that is hopping about there?"

They all looked. They saw a sober-brown neat little bird, hopping perkily on the grass.

"It's a sparrow—without a black bib," said Pat.

"Wrong!" said Uncle Merry. "It's a chaffinch."

"But chaffinches have lovely salmon-pink breasts," said Janet, at once. "Look—there's one!" She pointed to a bright, neat little bird with a beautiful pink breast. He had just flown down beside the other bird.

"That's a cock-chaffinch," said Uncle Merry. "The first one we saw is a hen-chaffinch, not a sparrow. Very often cock and hen birds differ in their plumage, Janet. You remember that we noticed the cock-sparrows had black bibs, and the hens hadn't? Well, the cock-chaffinch is gay with his pink chest, but the little hen is all brown. Don't mix her up with the sparrow. Watch the birds carefully, and you will soon know one kind from another."

"Cock- and hen-chaffinch," said John to himself. "I shall put those down on my chart!"

Someone knocked hard on one of the house windows.

"Time to go in," said Uncle Merry. "Well—your walk has done you all good! Your cheeks are quite rosy now, and your eyes are bright. I'll take you for a nice long walk when February is in. We shall find such a lot of things then. Good-bye for now!"

"Good-bye, and thank you," called the children. They went indoors—and in John's pocket was something else—three glued-together snails!

CHAPTER 2

THE WORLD IS SO FULL OF A NUMBER OF THINGS

ONE morning the whole household was disturbed by shrieks from John. The noise came from the play-room, and everyone rushed upstairs to see what the matter could be.

John was standing by the open window, sobbing, big tears pouring down his face. Uncle Merry, who was just coming in at the gate, was most amazed.

"What's up?" he shouted.

"My snails!" wept John. "A horrid big bird hopped

21

in at the window and took them one by one. Oh, my snails! I just put them there for an airing, and that's what happened. And I did like them so!"

By now everyone was in the play-room, listening to John's tale of woe. Fergus was most upset, and tried to lick John's hand all the time.

"A bird took your snails—how ridiculous!" said Janet scornfully. "How could a bird eat a snail, with its hard shell? You're just making it up, John."

"I'm not," said John fiercely. "I *saw* the bird. First it stood on the window-sill and had a look in—and then it picked up a snail and flew off. It was a big bird, and it had some freckles on its chest, like you have on your face, Janet."

"A thrush," said everyone at once. "But a thrush wouldn't eat snails," said Janet.

"Put on your things and come along with me," said Uncle Merry, "and I'll show you how and where a thrush does eat snails. I was coming to fetch you for your walk in February. Hurry up!"

John forgot his tears. All the children rushed to get their things on. Then they followed Uncle Merry out of doors and into his own back garden. He took them down to the bottom, and just before they got there he made a sign to them to keep quite still. "Listen," he said.

They all listened—and they heard a funny little noise—tap, tap, tap, knock, knock, knock. Tap, tap, tap, knock, knock, knock.

"What is it?" whispered John. Uncle Merry tiptoed a little further down the path and then pointed silently to a big stone not far off. Beside it was a freckled thrush, with a snail in its beak—and he was banging the shell hard on the stone to break it. Tap, tap, tap, knock, knock, knock!

"He is breaking the shell in order to get at the soft body inside," whispered Uncle Merry. "Do you see that stone? It is the thrush's anvil—the place where he always brings his snails. Look at the broken shells scattered around it. He has rid many a nearby garden of their snails!"

Tap, tap, tap—the shell broke. The thrush could now get at the soft body inside and soon the snail was eaten. Bits of his broken shell lay round about. The thrush flew up to the branch of a nearby tree, wiped his beak on a twig, and flew off. He had had a very good meal.

"Now you see how a thrush deals with a hard-shelled snail," said Uncle Merry. "Keep your eyes open and you may often come across a thrush's anvil, with bits of broken shell scattered around. Come along now—we must go for our walk. Look out for flowers as you go—there are a few more out. You will find chickweed and groundsel, of course, but we won't pick those this time—only new flowers."

They went down the lane. Birds seemed to be singing all round them. "There's the chaffinch calling 'pink-pink!'" said Uncle Merry. They listened, and clear and loud came the chaffinch's call "pink-pink, pink, pink!"

"Is that his song?" asked John. Uncle Merry shook his head.

"No—that's his call-note, John," he said. "The great-tit has a call-note very like it, if you listen. He calls 'pink-pink' too. The chaffinch's song isn't a bit like his call-note. It goes like this—'chip-chip-chip-cherry-erry-erry-chippy-oooEEEar! Chip-chip-chip-cherry-erry-erry-chippy-oooEEEar!'"

The children listened—and just then a chaffinch rattled out his "chip" song loudly and clearly. "Chip-chip-chip-cherry-erry-erry-chippy-oooEEEar!" Another answered him, and the children had no difficulty

at all in recognising the song, although they had never known it before.

They came to a little cottage outside which was a tree on which was hung a string of pea-nuts, threaded together through their shells.

"For the tits!" said Janet. "I did that once, and it was such fun to watch the tits coming. But I could never tell which were which."

"Well, we'll stand here for a few moments and see what tits come," said Uncle Merry. "I can soon tell you which are which! Only three kinds will come to this string of nuts."

They waited for a while—and then down flew a big, bold, bright-coloured tit, with glossy black head and yellow and green colouring. "Pink-pink!" he said, as he swung on a nut and pecked hard at it.

"The great-tit!" said Pat, at once, remembering that the great-tit and the chaffinch both said "pink-pink."

"Right," said his uncle. "Now here comes another tit. Is it a great-tit too?"

"No," said Janet. "He must be a blue-tit—he's so blue! Blue cap, and blue wings. How nice his yellow underneath is, against the blue."

"Yes, he's a blue-tit," said Uncle Merry. "He is a good deal smaller than the great-tit, isn't he? And now, here comes an even smaller tit—the coal-tit."

They all looked at the tiny bird that flew down to the nuts, swung himself upside-down and pecked busily.

"All the tits are acrobats," said Uncle Merry. "Look at the coal-tit, and see the difference between him and the others. Do you see his black head, with the line of white running down the back of his neck? His underparts are greyish-white instead of yellow like the blue-tit's. He is not nearly so bright in colour, is he?"

"No," said Janet, watching the three birds swinging on the nuts. "I shall easily know them all now that you've really made me look at them carefully, Uncle Merry. Big bird with glossy black head and yellow and green colouring—great-tit! Little bird with blue cap, blue wings, and yellow underneath—blue-tit! Little bird with black head and white streak running down the back of it—coal-tit."

"We may see the long-tailed tits some day," said Uncle Merry. "You can't help knowing those because they have such very long tails."

"I want to find a flower now," said Janet. "Oh look, Uncle Merry—haven't the lambs' tails grown long since we last saw them? Look—they are dangling from the hazel twigs, quite yellow now, and full of pollen. When I shake one, the yellow powder flies out on the air."

Janet picked a twig, and looked at it closely. She held it out to Uncle Merry. "See," she said, "there are some queer buds on this twig—they've got little red spikes sticking out of them. Why is that?"

"Ah—Janet has found a flower and doesn't know it," laughed Uncle Merry. "Clever Janet! Janet, the hazel tree has two sets of flowers—one of stamens, set in the catkins, full of pollen—and this queer little red-spiked flower, the female flower, which will make the nuts later on!"

They all looked at the red-spiked, bud-like knobs on the twig. There were two or three. "When the wind blows, the pollen is scattered on the wind, and some of it is blown on to these red spikes," said Uncle Merry. "Then this little female flower can make nuts for us to eat later on. Most flowers, as you know, have sepals, petals, stamens, and pistil all together in one head—but the hazel tree hasn't. It splits its flowers into two separate parts—the catkins and these red-spiked buds."

"Then the hazel doesn't use the bees to take pollen from one flower to another," said Pat. "It uses the wind. How clever!"

John was dancing along with Fergus. "Oh, look, Uncle Merry—there's another tree with catkins too.

It's a birch tree—I always know it by the lovely silver trunk."

There were little catkins on the birch, as John said —and when they came to the pond they saw catkins on the alder trees there as well. Janet was delighted to find a pussy-palm tree showing a little silver grey fur in its brown buds.

"Oh—pussy-palm!" she said. "I simply love that. Uncle Merry, have you a knife? Do, do let's take a little home, because it's such fun to watch the silvery fur push out further and further—and then, quite suddenly, it gets powdered with yellow and turns into golden palm. I really do love it."

"The pussy-palm has two different sets of catkins, growing on different trees," said Uncle Merry. "The hazel grows its male and female flowers on the same tree—but the sallow or pussy-willow, as we call it, has male catkins on one tree, and female on another tree."

"A sort of Mr. Tree and Mrs. Tree then," said John. "I know which the Mister Tree is—the one with the golden palm. I'm sure the gold is the stamens."

"It is," said Uncle Merry. "You can shake the pollen out later on. The Mrs. Tree catkins are not nearly so pretty—they are longer and greener. We will find them both next month. Here you are, Janet—here are one or two sprays of silvery buds for you."

"Uncle Merry—oh, do look—there's a *butterfly!*" cried Janet suddenly. "Oh, isn't it early? Did it come out of its chrysalis this month?"

"Oh no," said Uncle Merry, as they all watched the yellow butterfly flying along in the sunshine. "Some butterflies hibernate, you know, like the bats and the snakes—they sleep the winter away. The yellow brimstone—the one we are watching—does that, and so do the red admiral, the peacock, and the small tortoise-shell too. I have a peacock cuddled up in a corner of my bedroom ceiling. It has been there all the winter, sleeping soundly. Its wings are a bit torn and ragged, but when the sun warms it, it will wake up and flutter out of my window."

"It's nice to see a butterfly again," said Pat. "That's a creature that has an interesting life, hasn't it, Uncle Merry? First an egg—then a caterpillar—then a chrysalis—and then a butterfly. Four lives, really."

"Time to go home, I'm afraid," said Uncle Merry. "Come along. We may find a few more things on the way back. Do you see how nice and fat the leaf-buds on the trees are getting now? Even the beech buds don't look quite so sharp and pointed. As for the chestnut buds, they are really *very* fat."

"I should like some chestnut buds, please," said John. "I like their sticky feeling, Uncle Merry. There's a chestnut tree—look. Could you reach a few twigs for me?"

Uncle Merry was tall, and he soon had a few brown twigs to give to John. The boy felt them—they were as sticky as if someone had painted them with glue.

"What are these funny marks on the stems?" he asked, showing Uncle Merry some horseshoe-shaped marks. "They are exactly like tiny horseshoes. Surely no horses have galloped up these twigs!"

Everyone laughed. "That's where last year's leaves grew," said Uncle Merry. "When they fell off, they left those marks. They *are* like horseshoes, aren't they? Do you know why the buds are sticky, John?"

"To keep out the frost," said John at once.

"Quite right," said Uncle Merry.

On the way home they saw some white snowdrops in a cottage garden—and when they came to Uncle Merry's front garden, they saw that the golden crocuses were out, and that a brown bee was actually buzzing inside one!

"Ah—spring is really coming when we hear a bee humming," said Uncle Merry. "What a lovely sound! He is looking for nectar in the heart of that yellow crocus."

They said good-bye and went indoors. The children rushed to find their mother, and she was amazed to see all they brought with them. "I must say you are lucky to be able to go out with Uncle Merry," she said.

CHAPTER 3

MARCHING INTO SPRING

MARCH came in like a lion, roaring and bellowing. The trees shook and groaned, the clouds flew across the sky, and the children longed to fly their kites.

In the second week Uncle Merry sent in a message to say that he and Fergus were going for a good long walk. *Really* long. Could the children come, and what about John's short legs?

John was most indignant. "Fergus has much shorter legs, and *he's* going!" he said. "I'm going too."

So all three of them went to join Uncle Merry one fine windy morning in March. He was in his garden looking at the first yellow daffodil bud, and at the carpet of yellow and mauve crocuses that glowed everywhere. The bees were very busy in them now.

"Hallo, hallo!" said Uncle Merry, pleased to see all the children. Fergus danced round them in delight, giving funny little wuffs of pleasure. He had already heard the magic word "walk" and had seen his master take his stick from the hall.

"I want to go a long way to-day, right to the common," said Uncle Merry. "It will be a lovely walk, with all kinds of things to see. Come along."

Off they went. The birds were singing madly all around, and the children proudly picked out their songs, for they had been very busy listening to them the last two weeks.

"Chaffinch!" said John, as he heard a bird beginning the familiar "chip-chip-chip" sound.

"Thrush!" said Janet, as a bird nearby in a tree sang "Ju-dee, Ju-dee!"

"Starling!" said Pat, as a fizzling and gurgling and whistling came from the roof of a cottage.

"Good children!" said Uncle Merry, pleased. "You are worth taking out for walks, I must say. Isn't it a lovely day? I feel like singing and whistling too!"

"Uncle Merry, I saw some snails awake on our rockery yesterday," said John. "I picked one up, and he hadn't got a hard front door any more, he was just soft and slimy underneath. Why does he leave a silver trail when he walks?"

"Well, when he travels over hard surfaces, he sends out a slimy trail to help him along," said Uncle Merry. "He's a funny creature, isn't he? Did you know that he had eyes at the tops of his horns? He rolls them in and out just as you roll a stocking in and out."

"Oh—fancy having eyes on horns!" said Pat, astonished. "I'll look very carefully at a snail's horn next time, Uncle Merry."

CELANDINES

"We haven't picked any new flowers yet," said Janet, skipping along, with Fergus trying to snap at her shoe-laces. "Don't Fergus! You'll trip me up!"

The children began to look about them on the ground as they walked. They must find some new

31

flowers to take home! They soon found plenty, for now, with every new week of the year, fresh flowers opened.

"What's this?" asked Janet, stopping by a plant that had tiny strings of green flowers. "Green flowers! How funny!"

"That's dog's mercury," said Uncle Merry. "You remember how the pussy-palm had male flowers or catkins on one tree, and the female flowers on the other? Well, the dog's mercury is a plant that follows the same plan. This one you are looking at is the male flower. The wind shakes the green string and sends the pollen flying off to find the female flower, which no doubt we shall find soon. It hasn't long strings like this one."

"Why are the flowers *green*?" asked Pat.

"Well, if you think a minute you will soon guess why," said Uncle Merry. "Flowers only make themselves colourful, and produce big petals and plenty of nectar when they want the bees to come and carry their pollen from one flower to another. Flowers that are wind-pollinated don't need to attract the wind—it is always there. As it has no eyes or nose or taste, the plants don't need to grow coloured petals or make tempting nectar."

"Oh, I see," said Pat. "Look—celandines! Aren't they lovely? All polished and shining."

They had come across a sheltered place where the golden celandines grew in quite a sheet. They spread open their golden stars to the warm March sun, and their petals really did look as if they were polished, or enamelled.

"Do they belong to the Buttercup Family?" asked Janet. "They look a bit like buttercups."

"This lesser celandine does," said Uncle Merry. "It belongs to the Ranunculacae Family—what a word for you! Now look—who knows what family this little flower belongs too?"

He picked a flower nearby. It had a pink very hairy stalk, and its leaves were beautifully scallopped round the edge, and were very hairy too. Its flowers, set by the leaves, were purplish-blue, and divided into lips.

"The Lip Family, the Lip Family," shouted John at once, and he felt the square stem.

"Labiate," said Janet, feeling rather grand.

"It's ground ivy," said Pat. "It's not a bit like ivy though, is it?"

"Not a bit," said Uncle Merry. "Yes, it's ground ivy—see what a lot of it there is. It grows everywhere in the spring-time."

"There's a little tree in leaf already," said Janet. "What is it?"

"An elder tree," said Uncle Merry. "It is always one of the first to put out its leaves. We shall find the flat clusters of strong-smelling flowers later on—and in the autumn we shall see the masses of purple berries that it bears."

"There are many more dandelions and daisies about now," said Pat. So there were. The big golden heads and the yellow-eyed daisies showed in many places. John's eye caught sight of a new flower as he passed by a tall hedge.

"Wait!" he called. "New flower! Wait!"

They all waited whilst he picked it. "Well, we have passed about twenty of these already," said Uncle

Merry, with a laugh. "I was wondering when someone would notice it."

"It belongs to the Cross Family—Cruciferae," said Pat, at once. "You can tell that by the four petals, set crossways, opposite one another."

"Quite right," said Uncle Merry, pleased. "This is Garlic-mustard, or Jack-by-the-hedge, a very common flower indeed. See its clusters of white flowers and buds at the very top of the plant, and its large heart-shaped leaves. Let me crush some leaves in my hand— there, smell them. What does my hand smell of?"

"Garlic," said Pat at once. And so it did!

"Jack-by-the-hedge," said Janet. "I like that name."

"Look out for new flowers as we go through the wood," said Uncle Merry. "We are sure to find some there."

They did. A squeal from Janet meant the first yellow primrose, set in its rosette of wrinkled leaves! The little girl picked it and put it into Uncle Merry's button-hole. "You really must have it," she said.

"I'll have a leaf too," said Uncle Merry. "It sets off the yellow so well."

"Aren't the leaves wrinkled?" said Janet in surprise as she bent down to pick one. "Is there a reason for that, Uncle?"

"Of course," he said, at once. "There is a reason for everything. The primrose leaves are wrinkled so that when it rains, the drops may run down the channels made by the wrinkles, and fall off around the *outside* of the plant instead of dropping on to the precious buds in the centre. You can see how the leaves are turned outwards, can't you, to take the rain away?"

34

"What a lot of clever ideas there are in the countryside!" said Pat. "I want to know them all!"

"Well, live to be a hundred, and you might know one millionth of them!" said Uncle Merry.

The children found sweet violets hidden under their dark green leaves and were able to pick a beautiful little bunch to take home. They saw many graceful wood anemones, swinging and swaying on their pinkish stalks, dainty and sweet.

"What lovely little flowers!" said Janet. "They seem to dance with the wind itself!"

"Then you won't be surprised to know that another name for them is windflower," said Uncle Merry. "Can anyone tell what flower family it belongs to?"

The children looked at the dainty windflower. "It's a bit like a white buttercup," said Pat.

"Good boy," said his Uncle. "It belongs to the Buttercup Family—Ranunculacae. We'll look it up when we get home."

Uncle Merry had shown the children his flower-book and they liked it very much. They thought it was fun to find the flowers in his book and read all about them.

"And now we are coming to the common," said Uncle Merry. "What a long walk we have had!"

They came to a warm part of the common and sat down in the heather. Nearby was a sandy bank. Janet looked at it and gave a shrill scream that made the others jump.

"A snake! A snake!" she cried. "Oh, the horrible thing! Kill it, Uncle Merry, quick!"

Uncle Merry looked really cross. "Don't be stupid,

Janet," he said. "That isn't even a snake—it's a lizard —a slow-worm or blind-worm!"

The children gazed at the blind-worm, thinking that it really did look like a snake. But they believed Uncle Merry when he said that it was only a legless lizard. "It is quite harmless," he said. "Wait a minute. I will see if I can catch it for you."

He slid silently to the sandy bank, and then, with a quick dart, closed his hand over the blind-worm. He showed it to the children. Its bright eyes looked at them as it tried to wriggle away.

"It isn't blind!" said Pat. "It's got eyes!"

"And it isn't slow!" said Janet. "It's quick in its movements."

"And it isn't a worm," said Uncle Merry. "Was ever a creature so badly named? It's a nice little legless lizard. There he goes—away into the heather. It's a good thing he didn't leave his tail behind. They some-times do if they are very frightened."

They all lay down in the hot sun. Soon Uncle Merry heard something unusual in the sounds of bird-song around him and he sat up. He smiled. "Ah," he said, "I thought I should see him to-day—one of the first of the birds to return to our country in the spring-time— the little wheatear. I heard his few notes just now."

Everyone sat up at once. Not one of the children even knew what a wheatear looked like. They saw a pretty little bird, with white on its tail and under-parts, and a black streak from ear to beak.

"There he is!" said Uncle Merry. "You can't mis-take his black streak! Welcome, little wheatear—you are always the first of the migrants to return!"

"Soon the swallows and martins will come back to

36

us too, won't they?" said Janet. "That will be lovely. And the cuckoo too. Oh—there goes the wheatear. I liked him. I'm glad we saw the first migrant."

"Well, we must migrate home!" said Uncle Merry, getting up. "Come on, Fergus. Leave a few rabbit-holes for other dogs."

"We've all got things to take home this time," said Janet. "You've got the first primrose, Uncle Merry. And we have all got flowers in nice bunches!"

"Fergus hasn't got anything," said John. "I'm sure he would like something."

"There's nothing for him," said Janet. "Don't be silly, John. He doesn't want anything."

"He does. He wants a flower too," said John, bending down to Fergus, who at once licked him on the nose. John put a flower into Fergus's collar, and looked proudly at the others.

"Look—he's got the right flower for himself—a piece of *dog's* mercury!"

And how they all laughed as they went home!

CHAPTER 4

MORE DISCOVERIES

ONE morning Uncle Merry saw three excited children rushing through his garden gate. He leaned out of his window and waved.

"Uncle Merry! We've heard the cuckoo! We've

heard the cuckoo! We've heard the cuckoo!" called Pat, in excitement.

"We all heard him at the same time," said John. "Oh, it was lovely to hear him again!"

"I heard him too," shouted down Uncle Merry. A loud barking from below the window inside the room told the children that Fergus had evidently heard the cuckoo as well!

"It's Saturday. Are you going to take us for a walk?" asked Janet. "This morning or this afternoon?"

Uncle Merry looked up at the cloud-swept April-blue sky. "This morning," he said, "I meant to do some work—but how can I sit indoors on a day when three excited children come and tell me that the cuckoo is back? I feel I want a day off. Ten minutes—and I'll be with you!"

So, with Fergus scampering madly round on his short legs, his tail wagging so fast that it could hardly be seen, the five soon set off down the familiar lanes, now green with hawthorn hedges on each side, and the golden celandines turning polished stars to the sun. John couldn't walk. He skipped, he ran, he trotted, he capered. He said it was too happy a day for walking.

"There's the cuckoo again!" said Pat, as the lovely double-note sounded on the wind. "Oh, it does seem like summer-time to hear that! I love the cuckoo, don't you, Uncle Merry?"

"Well, no, I can't say I do," said Uncle Merry. "He's not really a favourite of mine, except that I, like you, like to hear his call in the spring-time. But, you see, the cuckoo leads a lazy life—he leaves all the work of building a nest and of bringing up and feeding young ones, to *other* birds."

"Doesn't he make a nest then?" said John, in surprise. "I thought all birds built nests."

"Not the cuckoo," said Uncle Merry. "The hen cuckoo puts her egg in another bird's nest, first taking out an egg from the nest to make room for it. The

STICKLEBAT AND ITS NEST

bird who owns the nest doesn't seem to notice that it is a strange egg, and when it hatches into a bare, black, ugly nestling, the bird cares for it and brings it up as if it were her own."

"How queer!" said Pat. "It doesn't seem to be fair, does it?"

"No," said Uncle Merry. "The funny thing is that when the cuckoo nestling grows, it becomes much big-

39

ger than its little stepmother, and she has to sit on the baby cuckoo's shoulder to feed it!"

"Cuckoo! Cuckoo!" called a voice, and over their heads flew a big grey bird, with a barred chest. "There goes the cuckoo!" said Uncle Merry. "Probably she has only just returned to this country. She has spent the winter far away in warmer lands, feeding on the insects there."

"What other birds will be back soon?" asked John. "I know the swallows go away, don't they?"

"Yes—and the martins and swifts, the nightingales, the whitethroats, the chiff-chaffs, and others," said Uncle Merry. "Listen—I do believe I can hear the chiff-chaff now!"

They all stood still and listened. They had come to a little copse of trees in which many birds were singing. "What's his song like?" whispered John.

"Oh, he says his name over and over again," said Uncle Merry. "There it is—listen—chiff, chaff, chiff, chaff, chiff, chaff!"

They all heard it in delight. "Now I will always know the chiff-chaff's voice," said John, pleased.

They left the trees and went on, Fergus putting his head down every hole they came to. Suddenly Uncle Merry stopped and looked upwards, intense pleasure on his face. The children looked up too. They saw a steel-blue, long-tailed bird sweeping through the air, and a few more on the telegraph wires, making a musical twittering sound. "Feet-a-feetit, feet-a-feetit!" they said.

"The swallows!" said Uncle Merry. "Bless them, they're back again! How I love them!"

The children loved them too, as they watched them

40

flying swiftly through the air, forked tails streaming behind them. With them flew birds rather like them, but with a good deal of white about them, both underneath and on the back. Their tails were not so long.

"Are those shorter-tailed birds swallows too?" asked John.

"They belong to the Swallow Family," said Uncle Merry. "They are house-martins. They build their nests of mud, under the eaves of houses. You must have seen them. The swallows put their nests on rafters or beams in barns and sheds, and that is why we call them barn swallows. The martin up there is called the house-martin because he likes to build near our houses. There is another little martin too, brown and white, the sand-martin. He builds his nest in a hole in a bank or quarry, together with many of his friends."

"I shall never know them all," sighed Janet, looking at the swallows and martins. "Isn't there another bird like the swallows, Uncle—the swift?"

"Ah yes," said Uncle Merry, "but he doesn't come until a bit later. He isn't a swallow. He is rather like them to look at simply because he leads the same aerial life, and therefore needs the same kind of wings and long tail. He is sooty-black, not blue. I'll point him out to you when he arrives."

"There is such a lot to learn," said Janet. "I don't know how you remember everything, Uncle."

"Only because I love the countryside, and am always looking around and noticing things; and then, of course, because I love them I read about them in my books," said Uncle Merry. "You can do the same— and perhaps when you are my age you will know ten times more than I do!"

41

Janet thought that was quite impossible. She slipped her hand into Uncle Merry's and thought how lovely it would be to know so much and love so much. She was already beginning to understand the deep delight and intense joy he showed and felt in the host of things that made up the countryside. It was something only those could know who felt it themselves too— and Janet was beginning to feel it. She felt it when she looked at the sheet of golden celandines. She squeezed her uncle's hand.

"When I see things like that, I feel sometimes as if I'd like to write a poem about them, and keep them for ever!" she half-whispered.

Uncle Merry looked down at her, a wise smile in his brown eyes. "You feel as artists do when they long to paint something," he said. "They want to catch the beautiful thing their eyes see and keep it prisoner for ever on their canvas. Poets want to capture it and hold it imprisoned in words. Musicians entangle it in music. Janet, it is a precious gift to be able to feel like that. Let it grow!"

"Uncle Merry, what is that little bird over there— like a sparrow?" asked Pat, pointing to a small bird looking for insects in the ditch.

"It's not like a sparrow," said John at once, "except that it's brown! Look at its thin beak, Pat—sparrows have a big clumsy beak. That bird looks more like a robin."

"John, I sometimes think you are the sharpest of all you three children," said Uncle Merry. "You really do notice things. That bird is a hedge-sparrow—but, as you say, it isn't really a sparrow. You have only to see its beak to know that it is an insect-eater, not a seed-eater like the real sparrow."

They all watched the sober-brown bird. It made some funny little movements with its wings.

"It shuffles them!" said John.

"Its other name is Shufflewing," said Uncle Merry. "You can see why!"

"Uncle—it's flown up into that hedge there," said Pat, as the bird flew into a green hawthorn nearby. "Has it got its nest there, do you think?"

The bird flew out again. Uncle Merry went quietly to the hedge and parted a few twigs. He saw a nest there, with a sitting bird. The bird flew off in fright. Uncle Merry beckoned the children.

"I hate frightening a sitting bird," he said, "but you must really see one of the prettiest sights in the bird kingdom. Look!"

The children looked—and there in the nest were four hedge-sparrow eggs as blue as the sky above—the purest, brightest blue imaginable, gleaming against the brown of the nest-cup.

"Oh, lovely!" said Janet, her eyes starry with delight. "Quite, quite perfect!"

They left the nest of eggs for the mother to come back to, and went on their way. A big bumble bee sailed past and Janet nearly squealed, but not quite. Fergus jumped up at it in indignation, for it went very near his nose.

"Zooooom!" said the bee, and sailed away.

"He spent the winter sleeping in a hole in a bank," said Uncle Merry. "Lovely thing, isn't he, with his velvet coat of thick fur?"

"Uncle Merry, we haven't found a single new flower," said Pat. "Isn't that queer?"

"Not very," said Uncle Merry with a laugh. "We've been looking up into the sky most of the time, haven't we, and seeing the birds? We can't look down at the ground as well. But now we will. Come along—who will see a new flower first?"

John did, of course. His eyes never seemed to miss anything. Janet was a bit of a dreamer, and sometimes seemed to look at things without seeing them. Pat was full of eagerness and saw plenty of things, but because he didn't look at them carefully, like John, he made a good many mistakes.

"Oh, Uncle, I don't even know if it *is* a flower," said John eagerly. "It's the funniest thing you ever saw. First, when I saw it, it was a sort of twisted green sheath, growing straight upwards in the ditch. The next time I saw it the sheath thing was undoing itself, and then it looked like those things the old monks used to wear—hoods or cowls they were called, weren't they? And *then*, Uncle, a sort of poker grew straight up in the very middle of the sheath! What do you think of that?"

"*Most* extraordinary!" said Uncle Merry. "Show me this poker-flower, will you?"

John took him to a nearby ditch, and showed him a curious plant. From big arrow-shaped, purple-blotched leaves rose a strange "flower". As John said, it was like a monk's cowl or hood in green, and in the middle was a purple "poker", like a tall, round tongue.

"It's a bit like a tiny bulrush head, isn't it?" said Janet. "Whatever is it, Uncle?"

"It's a wild arum," said Uncle Merry, "a very com-

44

mon wild plant, and a very strange and curious one. It has many names—lords and ladies, cuckoo-pint, wake-robin, and it grows freely everywhere. The lords are the purple pokers, the ladies are the paler ones you find."

"It doesn't seem to have any stamens or stigmas at all," said Pat, picking a wild arum and looking at the tongue or poker.

"It has plenty," said Uncle Merry, and he stripped away the green sheath from the poker, and from below it too. The sheath bulged out there, and in the bulge grew stamens, stigmas, and hairs. "Look, two sorts of flowers, female and male," said Uncle Merry, pointing to the stigmas and the stamens.

"There are some flies in this bottom part," said Janet; "what are they doing there?"

"Ah, there's quite a story to tell!" said Uncle Merry. "This arum wants small flies to come and pollinate it. It wants pollen from another arum brought to its stigmas. So, to attract the kind of flies it wants, it sends out a nasty smell. Along come flies that like nasty smells, thinking there must be food for them somewhere, if there is a smell like that!"

"What do they do?" asked Pat.

"The flies creep into the sheath, and follow the smell downwards, past this bugle at the bottom of the poker," said Uncle Merry. "But alas for them—there is no nasty-smelling food down there to match the smell! They try to get out, but can't because the ring of hairs won't let them out. So they bustle about, cross and puzzled, and brush against these female flowers, the stigmas. They leave on the stigmas any pollen they have already got on their backs from other arums.

45

Well, when the stigmas have the pollen they want to make berries, and the stamens have *their* turn."

"*They* get ripe and send pollen over the flies, I suppose," said Janet.

"They do," said Uncle Merry; "and then the arum kindly sends out some sweet nectar which the flies feast on. That is their reward. When they have feasted, the hairs allow them to creep out—and off they fly to another arum, ready to pollinate the next lot of stigmas, when they are once more imprisoned below the poker."

"I really do think the flowers are clever, the way they work with the insects to get their pollen sent about," said Janet. "It's wonderful! They haven't got brains to think, as we have, and yet all these ideas are there, worked out to perfection. It's mysterious."

"It is—most mysterious," said Uncle Merry. "Look —there's the first cowslip! I really must mention it, because I feel *I* would like to claim a new flower, too, this morning!"

The cowslip nodded its head in the wind as it grew in the grass nearby.

"I know it belongs to the Primrose Family," said Janet, picking it. "Oh—it does smell sweet! There will be thousands of these out here next month, Uncle. We must gather a big bunch then to take home to Mother."

When they came to a chattering little stream, they found a lovely place under a willow tree whose fresh leaves shone golden in the sun, and sat down.

A flash of brilliant blue shot down the stream by them and all three children cried out in wonder. "What was that?"

46

"The kingfisher," said Uncle Merry. "Maybe he has come to have his dinner with us! He is fond of perching on that branch there, overlooking the water. Ah—watch—here he is, back again—and on that very branch too. What luck! We may see him fishing for his dinner."

The brilliant blue and green bird, his orange underparts glowing brightly, sat on the branch, watching the water. He had very little tail, which gave him rather a stumpy appearance, but his beak made up for that, for it was long and strong.

Suddenly he spied a fish in the stream, and dived head-first into the water. He was up again in a trice, a wriggling fish in his beak. A gulp—and it was gone!

In a few moments he dived in again—but this time he missed the fish. The children loved watching him as they sat by the water-side.

Then a little black moor-hen came up, her head bob-bob-bobbing as she swam over the water. When she saw the children she took fright, and disappeared below the water at once. The children laughed to see such a vanishing act.

"See her beak?" said Uncle Merry, pointing to a black speck moving across the surface of the water. "She is swimming under the water, where you see those double wrinkles spreading out behind her on the stream. She probably has a nest somewhere, a big platform on the flattened rushes, where she lays her eggs. She always covers them carefully when she leaves."

"Do you see that little spined fish?" Uncle Merry asked. "He builds a nest each spring, chases his mate in there to lay her eggs, and then keeps guard over them until they hatch."

47

"I never before heard of a fish that made a nest!" said Janet, in amazement. "What's it like?"

"Muff-like in shape," said Uncle. "Perhaps one day you will see one—you certainly would if you kept a pair of sticklebacks in an aquarium, and gave them bits and pieces to build a nest. Now I just want to show you the little creature I told you about that builds itself a house."

Uncle Merry scraped about in the mud in a certain place in the pond—and brought up two curious creatures. He showed them to the children. It looked as if he was holding two tubes made of bits of stick and tiny grains.

"The little insect that lives inside these cases has a very soft body that other pond-animals like to eat," he said; "so to protect himself, he gathers together any odd bits and pieces he can find in the water, glues them together, and makes himself this funny little house. There he lives quite safely, putting out his head and legs when he wants to crawl about, and able to hide himself quickly when enemies swim near."

"Do these funny little grubs turn into anything?" asked Janet.

"They are caddis grubs, the grub of the caddis fly," said Uncle Merry. "There will come a day when they crawl from the water, and fly away into the air, complete with wings."

The curious "houses" were returned to the pond, and the children spent some time in watching the water-snails on the weed, and some big black beetles coming up to the surface of the pond for air. The water was full of life, and the ramblers spent a whole hour watching the creatures that made it their home.

They didn't at all want to go home, but at last they had to. John found a robin's nest on the way back, in a very curious place. He saw an old boot lying in a ditch and when he went to look at it, there, inside it, was a robin's nest, with the bright-eyed robin sitting closely on it!

Then home they all went, tired and happy. The gorse was ablaze now, and was a magnificent sight. It sent out a glorious smell.

"Coco-nut!" said Janet.

"Vanilla!" said Pat.

"No—just lovely gorse, blazing in the hot April sun!" said Uncle Merry.

"That was one of the nicest walks we have ever had," said John, remembering the robin's nest he had found, and the brilliant blue kingfisher. "Wasn't that kingfisher lovely? I do wish he lived in my garden!"

CHAPTER 5

SUMMER IS HERE

By now the three children were really beginning to know how to use their eyes and ears, even when they were by themselves. They had only to go out into the garden to notice dozens of things—birds, flowers, trees, insects. Then on rainy days there were nature books to read, flowers or insects to look up and name, and many other things to do.

One morning John went into the garden and heard

the swallows twittering together. He loved their little voices saying "feetafeetit, feetafeetit." He looked up at them and saw that another bird was flying with them.

"That must be the swift," said John to himself. "It's sooty black, as Uncle Merry said. What great wide sickle-shaped wings it has! It looks like a flying anchor!"

Uncle Merry was in his garden. John called over the wall to him. "Uncle! I've seen a new bird to-day. I'm sure it's the swift. It must just have come back to this country this morning."

Uncle Merry put down his book and laughed. "Oh, John—the swift has been back a long time now! I didn't say anything about it because I wanted to see when you children would notice it."

"Uncle, are you busy to-day? Fergus would like a walk."

"Wuff," said Fergus at once.

"Which really means that *you* would like a walk, John, I suppose," said Uncle Merry. "Well, let me finish this bit of work, and I'll take you out for a little while."

On the very finest day that the year had yet shown, the five ramblers, including Fergus, set out happily together. They remembered how they had begun their walks in the bare bleak days of January, when it was a real thrill to find a flower of any sort. Now the ground was carpeted with scores of different flowers, the trees were in full leaf, tender and lovely, and insect and animal life was everywhere.

To the woods they went, and soon came in sight of a great stretch of bluebells. They all stopped to gaze at them, even Fergus.

"There's a picture for you!" said Uncle Merry, under his breath to Janet. "Doesn't it make you want to capture it and put it into a beautiful poem?"

Janet nodded. The sight of the shimmering blue flowers, shining there by the thousand, looking almost like a blue lake, filled her with such joy that she could hardly speak. She made up her mind to remember it all and make a poem about it when she was alone, and could think of the right and beautiful words that would capture the loveliness before her.

They picked some bluebells, and the sweet scent was delicious. John noticed that they had bulbs, like his snowdrops at home. He pulled one up and looked at it. "It's a bit like a little onion," he said.

"Yes, the onion is a bulb too," said Uncle Merry. "Do you see the fleshy leaves it is made up of? After the bluebell flowers are over, and are withering, the green leaves grow very long. They take in all the air and sunshine they can, and turn it into food, which they send downwards to make a new bulb. They pack the food into the new growing bulb, and then die away themselves. The food in the bulb feeds the growing flower in the spring-time, and lo and behold, when the sun is warm, thousands of bluebells spring up from the bulbs, and we get this wonderful carpet of blue!"

Another beautiful sight awaited the ramblers when they left the bluebell wood and came to the fields. The buttercups were coming out by the thousand, for it was a very good year for them. One field was already spread with what looked like a cloth of gold. Again the children stood and gazed with joy. Uncle Merry glanced at them.

"It isn't only the interest of the countryside we come

51

out to find," he said, "it's the beauty too, isn't it? We have seen two of the loveliest sights to be seen in our country to-day—a bluebell wood and a buttercup meadow."

The children knew some of the flowers themselves, of course. They knew the red and white clover in the fields, and Janet showed John how to pick out the tube-like petals and suck them to see if there was nectar in the tip. "The bees love that," said Janet. "Look how the outer flowers turn down and wither, Uncle, when the bees have taken the honey and pollinated them."

"Here's a dear little sweet-pea," said John, dancing up with Fergus. "It's such a tiny one."

"A vetch," said Uncle Merry. "As you say, it's a wild sweet-pea, and belongs to the big Pea Family. There are so many of them. A quiet half hour with your flower-book will help you to look for and recognise our commonest ones. Did you notice that the clover also belonged to the Pea Family, John?"

John nodded. "And here's another," he said, picking a flower with orange-yellow, pea-shaped blossoms. "What is it?"

"Bird's foot trefoil," said Uncle Merry. "You will see why it has that name later on, when the seed-pods form. They grow in a little cluster, and look exactly like a bird's foot."

"I'll look for them," said John. "Oh, uncle—look at that bush!"

They all gazed at a bush which was entirely covered with bright yellow flowers, which all the children at once recognised as belonging to the Sweet-Pea Family.

Pat opened his mouth and shut it again.

"What were you going to say, Pat?" asked Uncle Merry.

"I was going to say something silly," said Pat, and everyone laughed. "I was going to say it was gorse, but I see it isn't. There are no prickles."

Everyone laughed again.

"Pat is using his eyes at last!" said Uncle Merry. "This is broom, Pat. Isn't it lovely? It is a cousin of the gorse, of course. We'll pick some to take home to your mother. She will like it."

They picked some of the sprays. They were tough and Uncle Merry had to use his knife.

"Quite a lot of the Pea Family are out this morning," said John. "Oh, Uncle—look at Fergus. He's brought a flower for you to see too!"

Fergus had been rolling in a ditch, and some green plant had stuck to him. He couldn't get it off, and he was looking very disgusted indeed. He came to Uncle Merry to ask him to remove it.

"Oh, funny dog," said Pat, trying to pull off the green stuff. "Uncle, isn't this plant *determined* to stick to Fergus? What is it?"

"Goose-grass or cleavers," said Uncle Merry. "It *cleaves* or clings to us, or to any passing animal. It has very tiny white flowers—do you see them?"

"Why does it stick to us like this?" asked Pat, trying to get some off himself.

"It has a very weak, straggling stem," said Uncle Merry, "and like all plants, it needs to rise up to the light and sunshine. So it provides itself with tiny hooks that catch on to other plants, and enable it to raise itself upwards. A clever idea, isn't it?"

"Yes, very," said Pat, throwing away the last bit.

John immediately went to the hedge, picked up a handful of goose-grass and threw it all over Pat! It stuck to him fast, and Pat glared at John.

"Wait till I catch you!" he said. John danced away, giggling. "Just the sort of babyish joke he *would* play!" said Pat, making up his mind to plaster Uncle Merry's back with cleavers when he wasn't looking!

Uncle Merry had a little more to say about the goose-grass. "The goose-grass uses the hook idea for its seeds too," he said. "When the fruit is ripe, it is like little round green balls, very prickly. These balls are covered with tiny hooks that catch on to our stockings as we pass by, or on to our dog's coat. Then the seeds are carried away by us, and are shaken off in quite another part of the field! Thus the goose-grass makes certain of spreading its seeds."

"Another very good idea," said Pat. "The plants are awfully good inventors, aren't they? They seem to think of everything!"

"Everything except the wheel," said Uncle Merry. "They have used most of the mechanical devices that we ourselves have discovered or invented except the use of the wheel."

"We'll look for the goose-grass's hooked balls later on," said Janet. "We have a lot of things to look for later on, haven't we? Oh, look—is this a scarlet pimpernel?"

Uncle Merry looked down to the edge of the wayside, where a small and humble plant grew, set with vivid scarlet flowers. It was a dear little flower, and the children loved it.

"Yes—you can't mistake the scarlet pimpernel," said Uncle Merry. "It is one of our very few red wild

54

flowers. The strange thing is that many insects do not seem to see it, because they are colour-blind, and cannot see red. Another name for it is Poor Man's Weather-Glass, because it closes its petals in bad weather, and will only open them in fine spells."

"Well, it's wide open now, so it must be going to be fine!" said Pat.

"Aren't there a lot of insects about?" said Janet, as they went off down the lane again. "There are flies everywhere now—and little beetles in the grass, and yesterday I heard a grasshopper just near me, making such a noise. And the bees hum round all the time."

"I like watching the ants," said John. "I think they are very clever. Uncle, I watched some ants taking a dead caterpillar down one of their holes yesterday. The caterpillar was too big for the hole, so all the ants had a kind of meeting about it. They decided to make the hole bigger, and I watched them carrying grain after grain of earth away until they could get the caterpillar down the hole!"

"Yes—ants are amazing little things," said Uncle Merry. "Later in the year the female ants, which have wings, come out of the ant-hills and fly about in hundreds."

"I never knew that any ant had wings," said Janet, in amazement. "I must read about them in my insect-book when I go home. You'll be telling me next that earwigs can fly, Uncle!"

"Well, they can," was the surprising answer. "Earwigs have nice big gauzy wings folded neatly under their wing-cases, which you probably thought were just part of the earwig's back. Sometimes they shake them out—and then off they go in the air—flying earwigs!"

"Oh, dear—what a lot of ordinary things we don't know," said Janet. "But I'm sure I've never seen an earwig flying. I suppose they fold their wings under their wing-cases just as a ladybird does, Uncle?"

"Yes," said Uncle. "Look—here's a nice big spotted ladybird on this twig. We'll see if she will put out her wings for us!"

Uncle Merry let the brilliant little insect run on to his finger. When it came to the end of his finger it stopped. It opened its wing-cases, showing folded, gauzy wings underneath. It shook them out—and then sailed into the air.

"There you are!" said Uncle Merry. "There are many insects, like the bee and the butterfly, who show their wings all the time and cannot stow them away; and there are others, like the ladybird, earwig, and many beetles, who like to fold them up and put them away neatly when they run on the ground."

"Like we hang up our clothes in the wardrobe!" said John. "*They* put away their wings."

"There were many caterpillars to be found that day —hairy ones, furry ones, bare ones—green ones, orange and brown ones.

"Funny, greedy creatures!" said Janet, looking at some feeding on the green shoots of stinging nettles. "Always eating!"

"No wonder they grow so fat that they burst out of their skins!" said Uncle Merry. "But as they always have a fine, brand-new skin underneath, it doesn't matter. Soon these caterpillars will become sleepy, and lose their appetite. Then they will take off their

56

skins for the last time, and turn into little hard
chrysalids. Sometimes they will spin silk to hang themselves up by, cosy in their cocoons or chrysalids. Then
after a few weeks the hard skin of the chrysalis will
split—and out will come . . ."

"A butterfly or a moth!" chanted all the children at
once.

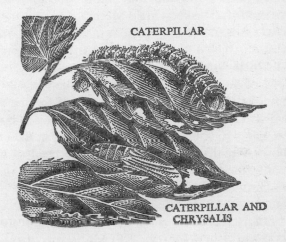

CATERPILLAR

CATERPILLAR AND
CHRYSALIS

"I'd like to take some caterpillars home and watch
all that," said John. "It seems like magic to me. Uncle,
how *can* a caterpillar go to sleep and wake up a butterfly! One a greedy, crawling creature, and the other a
light, beautiful thing with spreading wings! How do
the wings grow out of the caterpillar's body? Oh,
Uncle, it *is* a kind of magic, isn't it?"

"It's certainly very strange and very wonderful,"
said Uncle Merry. "Do you really want to take some
caterpillars home, John? Well, if you do, you must
take some of their food-plant home with you. They

will only live and grow if they have their right food. Nettles for some caterpillars—jack-by-the-hedge for others—currant leaves for magpie moth caterpillars—and so on."

"Look—there's a very, very pretty butterfly!" said Janet suddenly. She pointed to a white butterfly sailing along. It had pretty orange tips to its wings.

"What would *you* call that butterfly, Janet, if you had to name it?" asked Uncle Merry.

Janet looked at it, noticing the pretty orange patches. "I think I should call it orange-tip or orange-patch, Uncle," she said.

"One of your names is right," said her Uncle. "It's an orange-tip. Now watch—it is hunting for the plant on which its caterpillars feed. They like jack-by-the-hedge, the garlic-mustard we found earlier in the year."

The orange-tip fluttered down to the head of white flowers at the top of a jack-by-the-hedge plant. She sat there, hardly moving.

"Maybe when we come back this way we shall find her orange-coloured eggs laid neatly on the flower-stalks!" said Uncle Merry. "We will look and see, and if so, John can take the plant home, put it into a pot, and watch the eggs hatch into orange-tip caterpillars and feed on the plant."

"Oh, I should *love* that," said John. "I'll look when I come back."

Birds were still singing around, though the chorus of song was smaller now that so many birds were nesting and bringing up their young. Uncle Merry listened to the songs and then glanced around at the little company. "There is a new bird singing for us to-day," he said. "Can you hear him?"

"I think I can," said Janet at last. "It's a loud song —a bit like the thrush and the blackbird—there it is— pee-oo, pee-oo, PEE-OO!"

"Yes, Janet," said Uncle Merry. "That's it. That's the nightingale, another of our returning migrants."

"But the nightingale sings at night!" said John.

"And in the daytime too," said Uncle Merry; "sunlight or moonlight both stir him to song. I'll take you for a night walk in June and we will hear him then, if only he is still singing. May is his best month."

They sat and listened, but found it rather difficult to pick out the new song from among the other birds' voices.

They had to go home at last. John stopped by the jack-by-the-hedge, and to his enormous delight found that Uncle Merry had been right. There were tiny orange eggs on the flower stalks! He dug up the plant and carried it proudly home.

"I shall soon have a family of orange-tip caterpillars," he said. "I really am a lucky boy, aren't I, Uncle Merry?"

"Uncle, will you really take us for a night-time walk?" asked Janet. "It's full moon at the beginning of June. Shall we go then?"

"We will," said Uncle Merry. "We'll go on fullmoon night without fail—and we'll hope that the nightingale will give us a really good concert."

CHAPTER 6

RAMBLE AT NIGHT

THE moon was full on the second night of June. The children were tremendously excited, for none of them had been for a walk at night before. It seemed very thrilling to them.

John had to have a long rest in the afternoon, because Mother said he was too little to go out late at night unless he did. They were to start off at half-past eight.

"It won't even be dark then," said Uncle Merry, "and when the moon shines it will be almost as bright as daylight."

It was a lovely clear evening. The children went to have their supper with Uncle Merry, and they had it out in his garden. The beds were full of tulips and lupins, and here and there an early rose glowed red or pink.

"This is fun!" said Janet. "Uncle Merry, you really are a darling to think of such treats for us. I know we shall be glad all our lives long that we knew you this year!"

"That's the nicest thing that has ever been said to me," said Uncle Merry, pleased. "If I had a tail, you would see me wagging it nineteen to the dozen!"

Everyone laughed. Fergus wagged his tail as he always did when anyone laughed. He was having titbits from John, and was thoroughly enjoying the unusual meal out in the garden so late at night.

"Well, shall we go?" said Uncle Merry. "I think we had better, if we are going to be back before midnight!"

WILD ROSE

"Oh—do let's stay out till then!" said Janet. "It would be so exciting and mysterious!"

They set off. The twilight began to creep over the fields, but it had no chance to thicken into darkness, for the moon soon shed a brilliant light over the fields and hills.

"Isn't it lovely?" said John. "Aren't the shadows awfully black, Uncle?"

They went down the lane, over the stile, and into the field that led to the wood. Suddenly something that made a booming noise swung past Janet's face. She gave a scream. "Oh! What was that?"

Another boo-oo-oom was heard, and something flew straight into Pat's face. He put up his hand and caught it. It was a big red-brown beetle!

"Oooh!" said Pat, and dropped it. "What is it, Uncle Merry?"

Uncle Merry picked up the big, clumsy beetle. "It is a cockchafer or May-Bug," he said. "They often fly at night, blundering along with their booming noise as they fly from tree to tree. Another beetle is about now too—flying through the night air—the stag-beetle."

"Oooh," said Janet, with a shudder. "I hope it doesn't bump into me. That's the big black beetle with the funny antlers, isn't it, Uncle Merry?"

"It is," said Uncle Merry. "The 'antlers,' as you call them, are merely big, terrifying-looking jaws—but he cannot give much of a nip with them. He is a harmless fellow, and likes nothing better than to take a drop of honey from your finger."

"He won't take honey from *mine*," said Janet, with great determination. "I do hate things that buzz into me."

"I'd like to have a pet stag-beetle," began John. "I would give it honey each day. I would . . ."

He hadn't got any further than this before a big white shape swooped round a tree, and a weird and unearthly screech sounded just above his head. John clutched Uncle Merry's arm in terror, and Janet gave a frightened yell. Fergus growled and all the hairs on his neck stiffened.

"Uncle! Oh, Uncle, what was that?" asked John, trembling. "Oh, I didn't like it."

"It was only a barn-owl," laughed Uncle Merry. "You know that most owls fly at night, when their big

THE NIGHTINGALE

eyes enable them to see the slightest movement of mouse or rat in the fields below."

"I didn't hear its wings at all," said John, still clutching Uncle Merry's hand.

"No, because the owl flies so quietly," said his uncle. "It is well suited to night-flying with its big eyes, its silent wings, and terrifying screech that frightens any hidden animal into sudden movement. Its legs are feathered well down to the strong and powerful talons, so that even if a rat turns to bite, it cannot get its teeth into the owl."

"I thought owls hooted, not screeched," said Janet. "Oh, there it is again. I hope it doesn't screech!"

It did screech, but because everyone was expecting it no one was frightened.

"We don't mind you now, screechy owl!" said Uncle Merry. "Janet, listen—can you hear that lovely, long-drawn-out, quavering hoot? That is one of our owls—not the barn or screech-owl."

They all listened to the distant "Ooo-ooo-ooo-ooo!" that floated over the fields. It was a weird but lovely sound.

"There are more birds out at night than the nightingale," said Uncle Merry. "Come along. I want to get to the spot near which a nightingale nests every year. On this moonlight night he will surely soon be singing."

They all went on together. Janet watched for cockchafers and stag-beetles but did not see or hear any. She saw many pale moths, however, fluttering from the bushes, trees and grass.

Soon they came to the spot that Uncle Merry wanted. It was on a sloping hillside. He found a big gorse-bush which kept off the night breeze, and they all sat down on the wiry grass. As they sat down, they saw one or two scampering forms in the moonlight.

"Rabbits!" said Pat. "How lovely—they've come out to play!"

Fergus strained at Uncle Merry's hand, which was firmly on his collar. Rabbits! How he wanted to go and chase them! "No, Fergus," said his master. "Not at the moment. We want to sit quietly here and watch and hear all there is to be seen and heard. Lie down and be a good dog."

It was lovely sitting there in the moonlight. The trees whispered together now and again, rubbing their green cheeks against one another. An owl hooted in the distance. A moth settled on Uncle Merry's knee and then flew to Fergus's ear. He growled and flicked it off.

A sweet scent stole round the quiet company. Janet began to sniff. "Uncle! What is it?"

"There must be a few early wild roses out somewhere near," said Uncle Merry. "And I believe I can smell honeysuckle! It always smells sweetest in the evening. Still, it is very early."

"It's lovely sitting here in the moonlight, smelling wild roses and honeysuckle, listening for the nightingale," said Janet dreamily. "This would make another good poem, wouldn't it, Uncle Merry?"

From somewhere overhead there came a curious sound that made Fergus throw back his ears and growl deeply in his throat. The children looked up in surprise. The noise came again—a vibrating, jarring, churring noise, curious to hear. Whatever could it be?"

"Fergus thinks it's a dog growling at him somewhere in the sky," said John, with a laugh. "Oh, there's the noise again—chur-r-r-r-r-r. What is it, Uncle?"

"A bird is making that noise," said Uncle Merry. "The night-jar or night-churr! Isn't it a queer sound? The night-jar comes out at night, churring to himself. Look, there he goes!"

The children saw a long-tailed bird fly past, almost moth-like in its flight. It wheeled gracefully from side

65

to side, hunting for insects. Janet couldn't help hoping that it would eat all the cockchafers and stag-beetles round about! The bird flew to a tree and crouched down on a bough. It opened its beak and the churring sound came again.

"It's rather a nice sound," said Janet, "a churring, purring, whirring sound. I like it."

The bird churred again and Fergus cocked his ears towards it. Then off it flew into the air, silent and graceful. It disappeared down the hillside.

"Well, that was most unexpected," said Uncle Merry, pleased. "No, Fergus, keep still. We want to watch those rabbits play."

Suddenly Fergus growled again and looked towards a distant part of the hillside. Uncle Merry spoke to the children in a whisper. "Keep quiet! There's a red fox! Isn't he lovely?"

In the greatest excitement the children stared at the beautiful fox. They could see his graceful body, sharp, pointed ears and lovely bushy tail quite well.

"He's like a lovely dog," whispered Janet. "Oh, do be quiet, Fergus!"

But a fox as well as rabbits was too much for the Scottie. He gave a loud bark that sent fox and rabbits scurrying away at once. The hillside was empty.

"I wish the nightingale would sing," sighed Janet. "Oh—oh—oh! Uncle, WHAT'S THAT?"

She crouched against Uncle Merry, scared, as a small black creature with wide-spreading wings came fluttering near her. "Uncle, it's a bat!"

"Why are you afraid of a bat?" demanded Uncle Merry. "Just because of silly stories you have heard?

Has one ever hurt you? Can it sting, can it bite? You know it can't."

"Sorry, Uncle Merry," said Janet humbly. "I suppose it's just a habit I've got into."

"Well, get out of it then," said Uncle Merry. "There goes another bat, and another. They are hunting for

MOTH AT REST

BUTTERFLY AT REST

insects which they pop into a little pocket they have, made of skin."

"Uncle, their wings aren't made of feathers, are they?" said John. "What are they made of?"

"Just of skin," said Uncle Merry. "The bat has very long arm and finger bones, which act almost like the ribs of an umbrella, holding out the thick black skin of which the wings are made. When it goes to sleep, it hangs itself upside down, and passes the cold winter days away like that!"

"I think a good name for it is flitter-mouse," said

Pat. "Its body is very like a tiny mouse's, isn't it, Uncle?"

"Very," said his uncle. "Ah—now listen. At last we can hear what we have really come for!"

From a clump of bushes not very far off the voice of a bird arose on the night-air. It was the nightingale. It sang beautifully, pouring out its loud notes clearly, filling the air with musical sound. Sometimes it sang softly, and gradually became louder and louder, so that the children almost held their breath. It was a magical sound out there in the moonlight.

"Well, I couldn't very well hear its song when it was all mixed up with other birds' voices," whispered Pat, "but out here at night, when no other bird is singing, it is marvellous!"

From down the hill another nightingale began to sing, and then another. Soon the night was full of the exultant songs, and the children listened in wonder. They knew that they would never forget that night of moonlight and song.

Somewhere, very far off, a church clock chimed. The children counted the strokes. "Ten o'clock—no—eleven o'clock! Oh! Uncle Merry, aren't we lovely and late?"

"Too late," said Uncle Merry, getting to his feet. "I promised your mother to deliver you home before this if possible—but we had to wait for the nightingale."

Fergus flew off down the hill. The others followed more slowly, thinking of all they had seen and heard—nightingales singing—the night-jar churring—the owls hooting and screeching—the red fox—the rabbits—the beetles—what an exciting night!

CHAPTER 7

SUMMER HOLIDAYS

THE children were excited when they woke up on the first day of the summer holidays. Eight summer weeks stretched before them, weeks of picnics and walks, weeks of sunshine and warmth. Lovely!

"And a nice walk with Uncle Merry to start off with," thought Janet sleepily. "That really will be lovely. It's funny to think we never went for proper walks before—only when we had to take messages anywhere. To think of the things we never noticed! We hardly ever saw anything last year—what dull children we were!"

"Happy holidays!" said Uncle Merry, when he saw the children in the garden. "We'll go for a walk after tea—it will be nice and cool then."

It really was very hot now. The children lay and panted under the shady trees, and Fergus lay with them, his pink tongue hanging out. He seemed as much the children's dog now as Uncle Merry's, and they loved him dearly.

It was a little cooler after tea when they all set out, Fergus still hanging out his tongue. He didn't like the weather to be too hot. "You see, he can't take off his coat as we can," said John seriously to Uncle Merry. "I'd just hate to wear a fur coat in the summer like poor Fergus."

"Aren't the trees full and dark now?" said Janet. "They were such a bright tender green in the spring— now they are a very dark green."

"Let's go down to the lime avenue," said Uncle Merry. "The limes are out now, and the bees are in them. They make such a wonderful murmuring sound."

So they went to the little lime avenue, a pathway set between a row of common lime trees. They were flowering, and the children could see the little clusters of six or seven greenish-yellow flowers hanging down, guarded by a long, narrow bract.

"Oh, the smell!" said Janet, sniffing hard. "A bit like honeysuckle. Oh, Uncle, isn't it lovely?"

"And listen to the bees!" said John wonderingly. "What a noise! Uncle, there must be thousands up there among the lime blossoms."

"There are," said Uncle Merry. "The bees love the sweet nectar provided by the lime blossoms. We will come here again later on and see the little round green fruits of the lime. Just stand still a moment and enjoy the scent of the lime and the murmuring of the bees in it. The spirit of summer seems to be here in this little lime avenue to-day."

It was a lovely thing to do. Janet made up her mind to bring her mother there the very next day. "It's funny," she thought, "this is one of the loveliest things we've done this summer, and yet I've never heard anyone talk about it. We do miss a lot of lovely things through not knowing about them or noticing them."

There were such a lot of butterflies about that day. The children pestered Uncle Merry to tell them their names, and he told them the ones he thought they would remember.

"That's the common blue," he said, pointing to a pretty little blue butterfly. "And that's the ringlet—see the little rings on its wings? And that one you know—it is the red admiral. There's a meadow brown —we shall see plenty of those. What's that one?"

"Orange-tip!" said everybody at once.

"And there's a white cabbage butterfly," said Janet. "Oh, Uncle, look—is this a butterfly or a moth?"

"A moth," said Uncle Merry. "You have disturbed it by walking against it. It's called the Silver Y."

"Because it has a mark like a silver Y on its wings," said John.

"Quite right," said Uncle Merry. "Now—who can tell me the difference between a moth and butterfly?"

The children thought hard. "Moths come out at night and butterflies in the daytime," said Janet.

"Roughly, yes," said Uncle Merry, "but there are plenty of moths that fly by day too."

They thought again. "Butterflies fold their wings back to back, and moths fold them flat, when they're at rest," said John suddenly.

"Good," said Uncle Merry. "That really is a difference. Look at this silver Y—his wings are flat over his body. And now look at that red admiral butterfly resting on the hedge parsley. Do you see how neatly he has put his wings back to back, so that only the underparts can be seen?"

"What other difference is there between a moth and a butterfly?" asked Janet.

"There is one very big difference," said Uncle Merry, "and that is the shape of their feelers or anten-

71

nae, as we call them. Look at the red admiral's feelers
—do you see their knob-like end?"

"Yes," said the children, looking closely. The butterfly moved its feelers about almost as if it were showing off the knobbed ends.

"Oh," said John suddenly, "I know now—the moths don't have knob-like ends to their feelers—they have feathery ones—or thread-like ones. I've seen moths with lovely plumy feelers, almost like feathers."

"Right as usual, John," said Uncle Merry. "You can always tell a butterfly because its feelers have knobby or thickened ends—and a moth because its feelers are feathery, comb-like, or thread-like. And look at the way they fold their wings—then you will never make a mistake."

The children saw no more moths during that walk, but they saw plenty of butterflies, and noticed how they closed their wings, and what knob-like feelers they had. "I never thought of noticing little things like that before," said Pat.

They sat down on a warm, heathery bank to rest.

"Janet! Look—there's a snake near you!" said Pat suddenly. With a shriek of horror Janet shot upright. But it was not a snake. It was only the slow-worm, the little legless lizard that they had seen on another walk.

"How Janet loves to squeal!" said Uncle Merry. "Now, Janet, keep quite still, please, and don't utter even the smallest squeal—because there really *is* a snake near you, but a beautiful and perfectly harmless one!"

Janet didn't squeal, and she and the other two children looked with the greatest curiosity at the gleam-

72

ing creature lying basking in the sun. It put a forked tongue in and out.

"Will it sting?" asked Janet, in a whisper.

"Snakes don't sting," said Uncle Merry. "They bite. But we only have one snake in our country that can give a harmful bite, and that is the viper or adder. This is the grass-snake, or ringed snake. Do you see the patches of orange behind his head, making a bright collar? Look at his long tapering body—he must be nearly four feet long."

They all looked at the scaly, olive-brown creature. "Are you sure it's not an adder, Uncle?" asked poor Janet.

"Quite sure," said Uncle Merry. "Maybe we'll see an adder about here one day, and you will see that he has a blunt, thick body with a short tail—not a gracefully tapering body like this snake has. The adder is rarely more than two feet long. This poor grass snake is often killed in mistake for the adder—but even the adder does very little harm, for it will only bite when trodden on, which rarely happens."

"What does this snake eat?" asked John.

"Oh—small creatures such as frogs," said Uncle Merry. "Look at his unblinking eyes. Did you know that a snake can't close its eyes because it has no eyelids?"

"Poor thing!" said John, blinking his quickly to make sure that he could. "I wouldn't like it if I always had to keep mine open. Uncle—wouldn't it be fun to keep a grass-snake for a pet? Do you think I could?"

"No, John, no!" said Janet, in horror.

Uncle Merry laughed. "We shall never cure Janet of her fears, shall we?" he said. "Better not have a

73

grass-snake for a pet, John, because it would be difficult for you to feed it. Anyway, you've got plenty of caterpillars to look after, and that's enough for the present."

Janet heaved a sigh of relief. She did mean to get rid of all her silly fears sooner or later, but she just couldn't bear to think of having a snake living in the house as a pet. To her delight the grass-snake suddenly slid away into the heather and disappeared.

Fergus had been sniffing down rabbit-holes as usual, or he would certainly have tried his luck with the snake, for, unlike Janet, the Scottie was afraid of nothing. John was quite sure he would attack an elephant if he felt like it!

"Home again, children!" said Uncle Merry at last. "Come on, Fergus, home to supper!"

They gathered flowers on the way home.

"Oh, look!" cried Janet, in delight, "here is a bird's foot trefoil, Uncle—with its seed pods. Do you remember that you said we must look out for them when the flower had gone, and then we should see that the pod-clusters were just like a bird's foot? And so they are!"

"Another well-named plant!" said Pat, in pleasure, looking at the bird-like claw made by the bird's foot trefoil seed-pods.

Soon they neared home, carrying their "new" flowers with them. Janet made a face as she tried to avoid brushing her bare legs against plants scattered with little balls of frothy spit.

"Uncle, I do hate this spit-stuff," said Janet in disgust. "What is it? It's everywhere. Where does it come from? I don't like it."

"It's the home of a little insect," said Uncle Merry, laughing at Janet's disgusted face. "Look—I'll show you." He picked a grass with the "spit-stuff" on it, and with his finger parted the frothy spit. In the middle of it was a small green fat insect.

"Here we are!" said Uncle Merry, showing the children the little creature. "He doesn't like the very hot rays of the sun, so he exudes this froth to protect himself, and lives inside it. He is the grub of the frog-hopper, that nice little brown insect that hops on to your hand and then hops off again like a very tiny frog."

"Oh yes, I know them," said John. "When you touch them they leap right into the air, just like frogs. Frog-hopper—what a good name; and this is where he lives before he becomes a proper brown frog-hopper, Uncle! Well, I never guessed before that frog-hopper grubs lived inside these spits, looking so cool and green."

"We call them cuckoo-spits," said Uncle Merry, waving his hand towards the many dozens of froth-balls on the grasses all around. "I suppose people once thought the cuckoo made them, though I can't imagine why. John, what are you doing?"

"Just collecting a few spits to take home," said John. "I want to see how the grub turns into a nice brown frog-hopper that doesn't mind the sun."

Everyone laughed. John had a great collection of grubs and caterpillars and looked after them very well. Uncle Merry said that one day he would make a discovery that no one had made before, and John was always hoping that he would.

CHAPTER 8

A SEASIDE WALK

AUGUST came, and the days were hot and full of sun. Fergus became lazy and lay about in the shade. Even the children found it too hot to walk much.

"Well, well, well!" said Uncle Merry's voice, his head and shoulders appearing above the garden wall. "What a lazy set of children, all lying about on the grass. I suppose you feel too hot for a walk."

John sat up, but the others hardly moved. "Uncle, if only there was a little breeze!" said Janet. "The sun beats down, and we can hardly breathe."

"The only place for a breeze would be by the sea," said Pat. "There is always a breeze on the shore."

"Well, what about catching the train and going off to the sea for the day?" said Uncle Merry, most surprisingly. "It's only an hour away. Shall we go to-morrow?"

All three children were now sitting up straight, their eyes wide with delight.

"Oh, *Uncle*! Do you really mean it?" cried Janet. "A walk by the sea—along the shore—that would be simply marvellous!"

"Right," said Uncle Merry. "We all seem to be agreed about that. Ask your mother to get a picnic lunch and tea ready for you to-morrow, if she will, and we'll catch the ten o'clock train. There will be plenty of new things to see by the shore."

Everyone was excited the next day, even Fergus, who seemed to know that there was a train to catch, and somewhere lovely to go. At one minute past ten the five of them were speeding out of the station, off to the seaside.

"I want to find crabs," said John, "and some prawns, and shrimps, and starfish."

"And I'd like to find a jellyfish," said Pat. "Funny umbrella-like things, aren't they, Uncle?"

"I want to collect shells," said Janet, "and I shall find seaweed too."

"Woof," said Fergus. The others laughed. "He says he hopes to find rabbits, as usual," said Janet, who always pretended that she knew exactly what Fergus was saying when he barked.

It seemed a long hour before they arrived. They could feel the sea breeze before they got there, blowing into the hot carriage. They sniffed it happily.

"A breeze at last!" said John. "Oh look, there's the sea!"

The sea stretched blue and calm, meeting a sky that was almost as blue. White-sailed yachts sailed in the distance, and white-winged gulls soared overhead. The children watched in delight. The sea again! How lovely!

They tumbled out of the train as fast as they could at the station, and raced to find the shore. Janet took off her sandals almost at once. She ran to the shore, and then gave a sharp cry. She stopped and began to hop on one leg.

"Oh! Oh! Something's pricked me!"

"Well, look where you are going, Janet," said Uncle Merry, and he pointed down to the shingly sand, to where a prickly plant grew. "You trod on this sea-holly, and its sharp-spined leaves pricked your foot. Well, it's a funny way of finding a new flower, I must say."

The children looked at the beautiful sea-holly. It had bluish leaves, and bluish close-set flowers. "You can guess why it is called sea-*holly*, even though it doesn't belong to the Holly Family," said Uncle Merry.

John found four different shells.

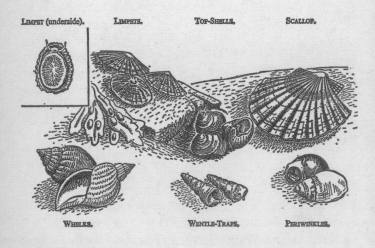

LIMPET (underside). LIMPETS. TOP-SHELLS. SCALLOP.

WHELKS. WENTLE-TRAPS. PERIWINKLES.

"I know this one—it's a limpet. It's like a hat, isn't it—a pointed hat; I like it."

"Yes—a limpet," said Uncle Merry, and he put it on his finger like a pointed thimble.

"You have often heard the saying 'Stuck tight as a limpet,' haven't you? Well the limpet can stick so hard to his rock that it is almost impossible to move him.

78

He's a shell-fish—a uni-valve, or one-shelled creature."

"What's this one?" asked John, picking up a big, prettily-shaped ridged shell, pinky-yellow in colour.

"The scallop," said Uncle Merry. "You must have seen these, much bigger, in fishmongers' shops. This creature is a bi-valve, or two-shelled animal. You have only found one of his shells. They are joined together by a hinge just here."

"Oh, Uncle—were all these empty shells once live creatures?" said Janet, in astonishment.

"Certainly," said Uncle Merry. "All the empty shells you find were once the homes of living creatures. Some of them had one shell to live in, others had two. The oyster has two, and also the blue mussels you see over there on that rock, holding tightly by little threads; and look, here is another bi-valve that John has brought, a very common one indeed—the cockle. When the cockle was alive, John, it had two shells, joined together at the back here by a little hinge."

John looked at the heart-shaped shell, and turned it over in his hand, imagining how it would feel to live inside two shells that he could open or close as he wished.

"Where does the cockle live?" he asked.

"The live cockle buries itself down in the sand," said Uncle Merry. "Have you ever seen sudden little jets of water shoot up on the shore? Well, those jets are sent up by the buried cockles. They dig themselves deep into the sand or mud by means of a large, fleshy kind of 'foot'. They use this foot for travelling over the surface of the sand too."

"How queer," said John, wishing he could see a live

79

cockle with a double-shell jumping about on the sand. "What is my last shell, Uncle? Is it a whelk?"

"Yes," said Uncle Merry, looking at the big, spiral-shaped shell with its pointed top. "A uni-valve, of course."

"Seaweeds," said Janet, taking one out of her pail of water. "Look, Uncle, this seaweed has funny little bladders set in it, that go pop when they are dry."

"It's the bladder-wrack," said Uncle Merry. "And this pretty misty-pink seaweed floating in your pail is the coralline seaweed."

John peeped into Janet's pail and saw some bright green, broad-leaved seaweed there. "Like lettuce!" he said.

Uncle Merry nodded. "Right," he said. "It's lettuce, or green laver. You can find a purple one in the pools too, if you look."

"And what is this last seaweed, Uncle?" asked Janet, holding up a big frond many feet in length. It was a shining red-brown, and looked like glossy leather.

"Oar-weed," said Uncle Merry. "It only grows in deep water, but sometimes a storm tears it up and then the waves fling it on the shore, where we find it."

One shell the children knew quite well, because it was a dark-blue periwinkle, often seen in the shops. Then they found another, a bright orange spiral shell, very pretty indeed.

"It used to belong to a little sea-snail," said Uncle Merry, holding it in his hand. "You will find yellow or dark-green sea-snail shells too. These tiny creatures have the most extraordinary ribbon-tongues, set with hundreds of teeth which can rasp at seaweed."

Janet found one more shell, a very graceful one, spiralling narrowly up to a sharp point.

"It's a ladder-shell, turning-stair shell, or wentle-trap," said Uncle Merry. "I think they are almost the prettiest shells on the beach."

The sea splashed over John's feet and he laughed. "I'm going to paddle again," he said, and off he went. Soon all three children, and Fergus too, were splashing in the waves. Fergus enjoyed himself thoroughly and barked at every foam-topped wave that broke near him.

Uncle Merry watched the big gulls again. He said that he could look at their graceful gliding all day long. Janet came to sit beside him.

"There is our commonest gull," said Uncle Merry, pointing to a big gull with a dark-brown head, and deep red bill and legs. "He is called the black-headed gull because of his dark head."

"What is that very big gull?" asked Janet, pointing to a pearly-grey bird with flesh-coloured legs and a yellow beak. "I've often seen that gull too."

"Yes, he's a very common gull as well," said Uncle Merry. "He is called the herring gull; and that gull with the dark back and wings is the black-backed gull. We have quite a number of different gulls, as you see."

The two of them watched the big gulls glide high on outstretched wings. "I wish I could do that," said Janet. "It looks lovely, doesn't it, Uncle Merry?"

"I've found a jellyfish!" shouted Pat, and he raced to where a round blob of jelly lay on the sand. "Look, Uncle! I'll put it into this pool. There!"

He slipped the curious creature into a deep pool nearby, and everyone watched its "umbrella" open. A fringe of tentacles hung down from the under-surface as the jellyfish swung like a big mushroom in the water.

"Those tentacles can sting painfully," said Uncle Merry. "They will not hurt us because we are too big, but any small creature bumping up against them will be badly stung and taken by the jellyfish for his dinner."

"Uncle, I was once stung by a jellyfish; really I was," said Janet.

"Ah, yes—but not this kind," said Uncle Merry. "There is a bigger, yellow-brown jellyfish which sometimes comes in-shore by the hundred, and can sting bathers very badly."

"Uncle Merry, what are these lumps on the rock here that look like red or green currant jelly?" asked John, in surprise. Everyone looked.

As they watched, one or two of the jelly-like lumps swelled a little and opened a pretty fringe all round the top edge. This fringe waved in the water like the petals of a flower.

"Sea anemones," said Janet. "Aren't they pretty? Uncle, are they flowers?"

"No," said Uncle Merry. "They are just a bag of flesh with a fringe of hollow feelers. Put your finger to those feelers, Janet, and see how they cling to you. Then you will know how the sea anemone gets its food. Any small creature that comes within reach of those feelers is drawn into the stomach of the anemone —and that is the end of him!"

"I don't want to put my finger there," said Janet, half afraid that the anemone would take it and eat it! But John and Pat had no such fears. First one and then the other placed his finger on the waving feelers and felt the tight clutch of the tentacles, trying to draw their fingers into the fleshy bag below.

"Uncle, let me give the anemone this tiny shell to eat," said John suddenly. He popped a small shell on the top of the anemone's feelers. They closed over it, and in a trice it was dragged down into the fleshy bag below, which was the curious creature's stomach.

But the anemone didn't like the shell! In a very short while it opened its feelers again, and out came the empty shell. This made the children laugh. John wanted to go on feeding the anemone with things it didn't want—"So that I can see it spit them out," he said—but Uncle Merry wouldn't let him.

In the same pool there were a good many shadowy, sandy-coloured creatures.

"Shrimps!" said Pat. "Where's my net?"

He caught a few, and put them into his pail. Everyone gazed down at them. Fergus tried to see too, and nearly upset the pail.

The shrimps darted about and John laughed to see how they sometimes shot backwards very suddenly.

"They don't swim with their front legs," said Uncle Merry. "They swim with funny little fringed legs at the back called swimmerets—and their strong tail helps them too, especially when they want to dart backwards."

"Let's put them back into this shallow pool where we can watch them better," said Pat. So the shrimps were emptied there—but no sooner were they in the water than they all swam down to the sand, burrowed into it, sending up a little cloud of sand over their bodies, and then lay quite still, with the falling grains covering them and hiding them.

"How clever!" said Janet. "Oh, Uncle—look—there's a very big shrimp!"

"It's a prawn," said Uncle Merry. "Now don't tell me that prawns are red—they only go that colour when they are boiled. He's a fine big fellow, isn't he?"

"I don't know how you tell whether he's a prawn or a very big shrimp," said John.

"Quite easy!" said Uncle Merry. "Do you see that spike sticking out among his feelers? The shrimp has one too. Well, if you feel the prawn's, or look at it closely, you will see that it has a saw-edge. The shrimp's hasn't. Look at the prawn's curious eyes. Do you see them?"

"Uncle—are they on the ends of those stalks?" said Janet, in astonishment, seeing two black things on stalks. "Oh, how queer!"

"Stalked eyes!" said John. "Fergus, how would you like stalked eyes? You could poke them down into rabbit-holes and frighten all the rabbits."

Everyone laughed. "Don't be so silly, John," said Pat. "Oh—there's a crab. Goodness, how it scuttles along, all sideways. I like crabs."

Uncle Merry picked one up. It tried to nip his hand with its little clawed foot. "Funny creature!" said Uncle Merry. "I see you have a nice new coat! I suppose you jumped out of your old one a day or two ago!"

The children stared. "How can a crab get out of its hard, shelly coat?" asked John. "It can't unbutton it, or unhook it!"

"No—it splits it," said Uncle Merry. "Like the
84

caterpillar, it often grows too big for its outer covering, and it bursts it. The crab has a soft body inside this shell, and he knows quite well that enemies would like to eat him when he wears no armour. So when he knows he is going to burst his shell, he hides himself away. His new shell takes a little while hardening over his soft body, and until that is done, and he feels safe, he does not come out of his hiding-place. When he does come out, I am sure his friends don't know him, for he is very much bigger."

The crab scuttled away when Uncle Merry put him down. He found a nice soft patch of sand, and sank down into it. In a moment there was no sign of him at all. He was gone!

"Whatever would a crab do if he didn't wear a shell?" asked John. "I do think it's a good idea to wear armour like that."

"We've seen a lot of queer creatures to-day," said Pat. "Uncle, it's lunchtime already. What about some sandwiches and a drink? I'm terribly thirsty."

They all enjoyed their lunch very much, especially Fergus, who as usual got a good many titbits from generous John. The gulls came swooping down to see if there was any bread to spare.

Then Pat found the first starfish. He picked it up and called to the others. They went to Uncle Merry with it. "Ah, a starfish!" he said. "Good. This is another queer creature—just five fingers and a stomach."

"Uncle, it was getting along over the sand when I saw it," said Pat. "But how can it walk? It hasn't any legs."

Uncle Merry turned the starfish over and showed the children his under-part. "On the under-part of his

85

fingers he has hundreds of little fleshy tubes that come out of holes," he said. "He uses these as suckers, and gets along with them, putting out first one batch and then another, so that he drags himself along quite easily."

"What does he eat?" asked Janet, who didn't very much like the starfish and his hundreds of queer "legs".

"Oh, shellfish, small crabs, anything it can get hold of," said Uncle Merry. "It is a greedy creature. If by any chance it loses one of its fingers it will grow another. Put it down on the wet sand and we will watch it walk off."

It was queer to see the starfish making its way along the sand. It went to a nearby rock-pool, and Pat saw it poking about under the crevices there, trying to find a meal.

Nobody found anything new after that, except a long, narrow shell that Uncle Merry said was a razor-shell, because it was like an old-fashioned razor case; and Janet found some more seaweed, dark red and fronded into fingers, which Uncle Merry said was dulse. He added that many people ate it, but Janet didn't think she would try.

The children were sad when the time came to go home once more. Seaside rambles were the best of all, they thought. They loved the sound of the sea, the feel of the strong breeze, the coolness of the waves, and the many queer creatures they could so easily find. Even Fergus was sad to go, for he loved chasing the waves as they broke on the sands and wetted his paws.

"Well, all good things come to an end," said Uncle Merry, taking John's hand. "Let's take home some of that ribbon seaweed, shall we—there's a lovely piece there with frilled edges. It is one of the seaweeds called tangles. It will tell us when the weather is going to be damp or dry. You shall hang it outside your bedroom window, Janet."

Off they went to catch their train, chattering about starfish, and jellyfish, crabs, and prawns, and shrimps, sea urchins, and sea anemones. What a lovely day!

Janet hung up her seaweed, and it at once became hard and dry. "Fine weather still," she said to the others. "Look at my seaweed. We'll have a fine walk in September, no doubt about that!"

CHAPTER 9

EARLY IN THE MORNING

THE children talked a great deal about their seaside ramble, and wished they could go again in September; but Uncle Merry said that there were so many things to be seen in the countryside that month, they really must go walking there.

"September is such a lovely time," he said to the children. "The rush and hurry of summer is over; the birds and animals have brought up their young ones; the plants have flowered and produced their seeds; everything is at peace, ready for the calm of autumn, and the sleep of winter. I think our next walk shall be in the very early morning," said Uncle Merry.

"Oh, Uncle Merry—yes!" said Pat, and the others

skipped in delight. I love going out very early. What time? Six o'clock?"

"Yes," said Uncle Merry. "That will be a lovely thing to do, won't it? We have been for walks at all times of the day except the very early morning. We'll see what *that's* like now! I hope you will all wake up when the day comes!"

"Of *course* we will!" said John. "I wouldn't miss a walk as early as that for anything!"

The early morning walk was planned for the last week in September.

Fergus woke them that morning by barking under their windows. John awoke and rushed to the window. Uncle Merry was below.

"Sleepy-heads!" said Uncle Merry, in a low voice. "Hurry down, or I shan't wait!"

In four minutes all the children were rushing down the lane after Uncle Merry and Fergus.

"Oh, Uncle Merry, isn't it a simply *beau*tiful morning?" cried Janet, catching up with her uncle, and hanging on to his arm. "Uncle, there isn't a cloud in the sky, and not a breath of wind either. Isn't the sun low?"

"Well, it has hardly risen!" said Uncle Merry. "Look how long the shadows of the trees are now, as long as in the evening-time, but now of course they stretch in the opposite direction."

The dew was very heavy indeed on the grass, and the children's feet would have been soaked if Uncle Merry had not warned them to put on their rubber boots. As the sun rose higher, the dew gleamed on the fields like a great silver sheet. Janet stood and looked at it. One more lovely picture to store away in her memory!

The trees were rapidly turning colour now and some of them were already beautiful. The big horse chestnut was becoming golden and russet. The elms were turning yellow. The limes were brilliant gold, and the hazels too.

"The world looks so clean and new on this early morning," said Janet, "and the sky looks as if someone has just washed it."

"Yes—the countryside does feel new and sweet in the early morning," said Uncle Merry. "Look—there are dozens of rabbits on that hillside. Come back, Fergus! Let us watch them for a while."

"Uncle," said John, as they went on their way, "do you see all these gleaming silvery threads everywhere? What are they? They catch on my face as I walk. They are like very, very fine spider threads."

"I was wondering when someone was going to say something about this beautiful gossamer," said Uncle Merry. "It's all over the countryside this morning. Look around and see it, children. Can you see the silvery threads gleaming by the hundred across the fields everywhere?"

"Yes," said Janet, standing still. She saw the gleaming silken strands stretching from the ground into the air, from the nearby hedge, from bushes and trees—fairy silk, soft and silvery!

"Uncle, what is it?" said John, again. "Is it spider thread?"

"Yes," said Uncle Merry. "That's exactly what it is! It is gossamer thread made by young spiders who

89

want to leave home and go adventuring over the fields!"

"How do they do that?" asked Janet, catching at a long strand, and feeling it cling to her finger.

"Well, you know that spiders can spin silken threads, don't you?" said Uncle Merry. "They spin the silk from little things under their bodies," called spinnerets. The young spiders spin a very long thread, and let it go flying off into the air, growing longer and longer as they spin it from their bodies. Then, when the thread is long enough to bear them and carry them away, they leave go their hold on the leaf or stalk they are on, and allow themselves to be carried away into the air, pulled by the gossamer thread they have been spinning."

The children gazed at the hundreds of spider threads gleaming everywhere in the fields that warm sunny morning. So they belonged to little spiders who wanted to go adventuring, and spun themselves long strands of silk that waved in the little breeze and pulled them along like tiny parachutists!

"I'd like to do that," said John. "I really would. It must be fun to spin a long thread and then launch yourself into the air on the end of it, flying you don't know where! Lovely!"

They went on their way, the gossamer brushing against their cheeks and legs every now and again. Pat pointed to a big fly flying clumsily over the fields.

"A Daddy-long-legs," he said. "They are out again now, Uncle. Look—there are some more."

"Yes," said Uncle Merry. "They are the farmer's enemy. Catch a Daddy-long-legs, and we'll have a look at him."

90

It was easy enough to catch the heavy, slow-flying creatures, with their enormously long legs. Soon Uncle Merry had two of them to show the children.

"Do you see this one?" he said. "Look at the blunt end to its body. That shows it is a real *Daddy*-long-legs, not a Mother-long-legs! The females have pointed ends to their bodies. Look—do you see the pointed end to this one's body? It is a female, and will lay its eggs in the fields."

"Why has she got a pointed end?" asked Janet, who now knew that there was a reason for everything, and liked to know it.

"It is to help her lay her eggs," said Uncle Merry. "She needs it to pierce the ground. She makes a hole and then she lays her eggs. These hatch out into the ugly grey leather-jackets we so often find curled up in our soil. Later on, after their resting-stage, they hoist themselves up out of the ground, creep out of their brown cases, which we can often see left poking up out of the soil, and fly off as Daddy-long-legs or crane-flies."

"Why are they the farmer's enemy?" asked Janet.

"Because the grubs eat the roots of the farmer's crops," said Uncle Merry. "They can do great damage."

John was busy looking at something a little way off. His eyes shone brightly, and he beckoned to the others.

"Here is something magic!" he said excitedly, and he pointed down to the ground. "A fairy ring! See where the fairies danced last night!"

Everyone looked down at the ground, where the grass shone deep, rich green in a ring. Uncle Merry laughed. "Yes," he said, "it does look as if fairy feet

91

have been dancing there, making a ring of deeper green grass where they danced!"

Pat didn't believe in fairies. "What *did* make that round ring of dark-green grass?" he asked, in curiosity. "There must be some reason for it, Uncle. I've seen dark rings of grass like that before."

"Well, a relation of our mushroom, the champignon or fairy-ring toadstool, caused that ring," said Uncle. "First, a spore blew there, the spore of a toadstool. It grew up into a toadstool one night. Its own spores ripened and were shot out all around it in a ring. Then the first toadstool died down."

"And all the new ones grew from the spores," said John.

"Right," said Uncle Merry. "They in their turn threw out their spores, and then died down. No toadstools could grow in the patch of ground where the old ones had been, so the fresh batch grew in a little wider ring, and the inside of the ring, where the first toadstools grew, was empty. Then these new toadstools flung out their spores, and again died down. No spores could grow inside the ring, so once again the ring became wider still."

"But why did the grass grow so dark and rich?" asked Janet.

"Because the withering toadstools fed it and enriched its roots," said Uncle Merry. "Where the toadstools had been, the grass grew rich and dark, and of course that deep green grass grew in the shape of a ring, because the toadstools themselves had continually stood in rings. And that's how these fairy rings of darker grass are made."

"I should never have thought of that," said John,

half sorry that there was no real magic about the fairy ring after all.

"This is a good time of year to look out for fungi of all kinds," said Uncle Merry. "You will not only find mushrooms and toadstools, but big puff-balls which dissolve into fine powder when you kick them, red-capped agaric toadstools in the woods, and many, many others. Some are beautiful, some are ugly, some smell horrible, some can be eaten, and many are poisonous. The fungi family is a very interesting one."

They found a peculiar flower, growing very high above their heads. It was very prickly indeed, leaves, stems, and even flower-heads being guarded by spines and prickles.

"What is it?" asked Janet, in surprise. "Isn't it tall, Uncle—taller even than you are? It's got mauve flowers. It's not a thistle, is it?"

"No," said Uncle Merry. "It's a teazel. It's a lovely, decorative plant really, with its big leaves, its strong spiny head, and long bracts protecting the flower."

"Uncle, look—there is quite a lot of water collected where the leaves meet together round the stem," said John. The others looked, and saw that the leaves formed a kind of basin round the stem, in which water had collected.

"That makes a sort of moat," said Uncle Merry. "The teazel does not want all kinds of small insects crawling up to its flower-head, so it grows its leaves round the stem like that in order to hold rain-water. Insects cannot pass that 'moat' and are drowned in the water."

"Yes, I can see some of their bodies in the water

now," said Janet. "Well, really, Uncle—I do think plants are clever!"

"I suppose the spines and prickles are to prevent the teazel from being eaten by animals," said John, "like the holly prickles."

"Yes," said Uncle Merry. "It's a pity I haven't my knife with me. I could cut a few of these bold teazel heads for your mother. They look lovely in a tall vase."

It was harvest-time. The fields of corn spread golden, far and wide, and the reapers were already at their work. In some fields the corn stood in stooks.

"Harvest-time!" said Uncle Merry. "Not only harvest-time in the corn-fields, but in the hedges where the blackberries are ripening, in the copses where the hazel-nuts will soon be ready to pick, and in the lanes and meadows where thousands of different berries are to be found. This is a wonderful time of year."

Janet found a bright blue flower which she liked very much. She took it to Uncle Merry. He took the tough stalk from her. It was set with flowers as blue as the September sky.

"We should have seen these, and some of the other flowers we have found, in August, if we had gone through the countryside instead of to the sea," he said. "This is chicory, a very common flower indeed about here, Janet, and a very pretty one."

"We seem to be finding new flowers, even though it is getting late in the year," said Janet. "Shall we go on finding them till Christmas, Uncle Merry?"

He shook his head. "No, there will not be many 'new' flowers to find after this month."

They went through the wood and came to a sunny hillside. They sat down to rest, and Janet gave a little squeal. She glanced at Uncle Merry. "That was a squeal of delight, not of fear," she explained. "A frog-hopper jumped on to my hand and off again. I was pleased to see him. He really was like a little tiny frog, Uncle, but harder."

Another frog-hopper jumped on to John's knee and squatted there, brown in the sunshine. John put out a cautious finger and touched him. He leapt high into the air and disappeared.

"We saw the beginning of his story in the cuckoo-spit, didn't we?" said Pat. "Now here he is at the end of his story. I do think insects have interesting histories, Uncle. Oh, look at that enormous bluebottle fly! Isn't he blue, and doesn't he make a noise?"

The bluebottle buzzed round, annoying everyone. "He's an enemy," said Uncle Merry, trying to catch him, "so is the housefly. We must always try to get rid of them both. They bring illness and dirt wherever they go."

"I suppose they start as an egg, hatch out into grubs, and then rest before they change into winged flies," said Janet, who was beginning to know quite a lot now.

Uncle Merry nodded and smiled at Janet. "You are becoming quite learned!" he said. "Yes, both the house-fly and the bluebottle have the same kind of history. The bluebottle of course loves to lay its eggs in meat, and when the grubs hatch out, they turn the meat putrid and evil-smelling."

"I think house-flies are horrid," said Janet. "I watched one once when I was out in the garden, having my tea there, Uncle. First it flew on my bread and butter. Then it flew to the dustbin, crawled under the

95

lid and disappeared inside. It came out again and flew to the jam; then it flew down to some manure on the beds, walked all over that, and flew back again to my bread and butter. Its feet must have been very dirty indeed by that time!"

"Yes," said Uncle Merry. "These flies bring disease to us on their feet, and we must prevent them from breeding whenever we can. Ah—I've got the blue-bottle. That's the end of him!"

But he hadn't! It flew out of his closed hand and buzzed round again. Fergus hated it. He cocked his ears and waited. The fly buzzed near him. Fergus snapped—and the fly was gone!

"Oh—isn't he good?" said John. "Fergus, you are very clever!"

Fergus looked at John as if he quite agreed. He licked the boy's knee, and then ran off to look for rabbits.

"The cuckoo has gone away now, hasn't he?" said Janet. "Have the swifts gone too, Uncle? I can't see them in the sky to-day."

"They will soon be going, if they have not gone already," said Uncle Merry, lying on his back and looking up at the blue sky. "The blackcaps and night-ingales are going too. It is sad to say good-bye to them —but they will come again another year."

"How do the birds know their way to distant countries?" asked Pat. "I suppose the old ones remember it and tell the young ones."

"No," said Uncle Merry. "Old and young birds go in different flocks, and at different times. The young cuckoos, for instance, are not yet gone, though their parents are. It is a mystery how they know their way.

Maybe the strong wind helps them, blowing behind them in the right direction in the autumn, and in the opposite way in the spring-time."

"I think it's another bit of magic," said John, chewing a stalk of grass. "I shouldn't know my way to South Africa, flying through the air—I know I shouldn't! I should have to get a magic spell to help me!"

"Well, let's see if you know your way home to-day without any magic," said Uncle Merry, with a laugh. "We are going, John. Jump up, or you'll have to migrate home alone!"

They all went home together, Fergus trailing after them, his nose sandy with sniffing in rabbit-holes.

CHAPTER 10

AN EXCITING RAMBLE

"AUTUMN is really here," said Janet to Pat one morning, as she opened her bedroom window and looked out on the garden. "Look how the trees have all changed colour now—except the evergreens; and the grass is already covered with fallen leaves."

"I like autumn," said Pat. "I like all the brilliant colours of the trees, the masses of berries everywhere, and the colour of the bracken in the woods. It's a nice time of year."

"It's a beautiful day to-day," said John, trying to look out of the window too, between Pat and Janet. "Oh, there's Fergus. Hi, Fergus!"

D

"Wuff!" said Fergus, looking up expectantly, his ears cocked and his tail wagging fast.

"Have you come to tell us that it's a good day for a walk?" asked Janet. "Well, you go and ask Uncle Merry, Fergus, and see what he says. Tell him *we*'re all ready."

Fergus ran off. "He really does understand what we say," said Janet. "Look, there's Uncle Merry! Uncle Merry, did Fergus give you our message about a walk to-day?"

"So that's what he came to say!" said Uncle Merry. "Well, can you be ready in an hour's time? I'll wait for you in my garden."

The children were pleased. Before an hour had gone by they were all in Uncle Merry's garden, and Fergus came to welcome them. Uncle Merry was looking at something, and they went to see what it was.

"Isn't this a lovely spider's web?" said Uncle Merry. The children saw that a big web was spread between some leaves on a bush. The spider who owned the web was hiding behind a leaf. The children could see her quite well.

"She's waiting for some insect to bump against her web and shake it," said Uncle Merry. "Then she'll be out in a trice and catch it. She will weave a webby coat around it, and then suck its blood at her leisure."

"Uncle, how can a spider make a web like this?" asked John, looking at the fine silken trap hanging in the bush. "Does she have web inside her, and can she pull it out as we pull cotton off a reel?"

Uncle Merry smiled. "Oh no, John," he said. "The spider has no web inside her at all. She has little lumps under her body called spinnerets, and out of these she squeezes a sticky fluid. When it reaches the air this fluid sets and forms a silken thread, which the spider uses at once for her web."

"How does a spider begin to make her web?" said Pat. "Look, Uncle—this web has spokes coming out from the centre, like a wheel has—and it has a spiral thread too, going round and round the spokes. I do think it's a very clever pattern."

"It is," said Uncle Merry. "The spider first of all makes the spokes, Pat, strong and firm. Then she makes the spiral thread, weaving it round and round the spokes. This thread she makes very sticky, so that a fly brushing against it is held fast."

"How clever some of these insects are!" said Janet.

"The spider isn't an insect," said Uncle Merry at once. "For one thing, it has eight legs, Janet, instead of six; for another thing its body is in only two parts instead of three; and, thirdly, the spider hasn't many different 'lives' as an insect has—it doesn't become a caterpillar, then a chrysalis, and then a perfect insect. It hatches out of the egg as a spider, and remains a spider. There is no grub stage."

"Oh," said Janet, "I always thought it was an insect. Look, Uncle—the spider has felt that fly shaking its web—it's rushed out to it!"

"Yes," said Uncle Merry. "It drives its powerful, poisonous fangs into its victim to paralyse it, and then it can tie it up in webbing if it wishes, and feast on it at leisure."

"Can it see well?" said John.

"Well, it has eight eyes, set in two rows on its head," said Uncle Merry. "We'll bring a magnifying glass out one morning and have a look at Mrs. Spider through it. You will be able to see her many eyes then, her fangs, which look like feelers, and her tiny spinnerets under her body."

"Oh, Uncle, look—a wasp has blundered into the web!" cried Pat, as a striped wasp flew straight into the silken trap. "It will break the web, won't it? Surely the spider won't try to catch the wasp—it will sting her."

"Watch!" said Uncle Merry. "You will see how sensible these tiny creatures can be."

The spider felt the wasp shaking her web. She rushed out and knew at once that it was a big and dangerous insect. She could not hope to bind it and catch it. It would break her web to bits if she did not stop it. But how could she prevent her beautiful web from being destroyed by the angry, struggling wasp?

In a trice the spider ran near the wasp, and began to cut away the threads that held it. One by one she cut them, and then, when the last thread was cut, the wasp fell to the ground, free! He cleaned himself up and flew off, grumbling loudly.

"Well, that *was* clever!" said Pat. "I suppose the spider will mend her web now, Uncle?"

"She will," said Uncle Merry.

Some thistledown came floating by, and John caught some. "Isn't it soft and pretty?" he said. "Is this the way the thistle sends out its seed, Uncle?"

"Yes," said his uncle. "I think, John, that instead of hunting for any 'new' flowers on our walk, I will set you all hunting for seeds and fruits, and make you tell me how the plants plan to spread abroad their seeds."

"Oh, that would be fun!" said Janet, who loved

having a competition of any sort. "I can think of heaps of seeds and berries already. Yes, let's do that on our walk, Uncle. I am sure I shall collect the most!"

"We'll see," said Uncle Merry. "Once upon a time I would have backed John to get the most, but you and Pat have really begun to use your eyes lately, and I'm not sure now who will win."

Uncle Merry told the children to run home for their schoolbags so that they might put into them the things they found on the ramble. Then at the end of the ramble they could be easily counted and sorted.

"I will keep a list in my notebook as you come and show me the things," he said, "and I will give you marks according to your common sense in telling me things about your finds. For instance, it would be a good mark if somebody told me how the squirrel helped the hazels to plant their nuts."

"*Does* he?" said Pat. He thought a moment and laughed. "Oh yes, of course! He stores the hazel nuts away in corners and crannies, doesn't he? And some of them must grow! So he helps the hazel to spread its seeds!"

"Quite right," said Uncle Merry, taking out a fat notebook and a pencil. "Now are we ready? No, Fergus—you are not in this competition, I'm afraid. You would only bring me bits of rabbit-fur!"

The three children set off happily, looking for seeds and fruits of any kind. It wasn't long before they found plenty!

"Ash-keys!" said Janet, bringing a bunch of the pretty "spinners", the winged fruit of the ash tree. "The ash sends them spinning away on the wind, Uncle."

101

"Good girl," said Uncle Merry, marking it down in his notebook.

"Conkers and acorns," said John, running up. "I'm sure the squirrel plants acorns too, sometimes, Uncle. Don't you think the satiny brown conker is lovely in its prickly case!"

"I do," said Uncle Merry. John gave him some hazel nuts as well, and some beech-mast. Uncle Merry noted everything down.

Pat brought a spray of blackberries, and a bunch of rowan or mountain ash berries, very beautiful in their coral red. "I think the birds spread the rowan berries," he said. "I saw some of them in the rowan trees, eating them, Uncle."

"Good mark," said his uncle, smiling. "Hurry up, all of you. I want many more things down."

Janet brought thistledown and dandelion clocks. Pat brought purple elderberries, crimson hips and scarlet haws from the wild rose. John brought a big spray of old man's beard, and showed his uncle how each seed was growing a plume of fine silken hairs to fly away on.

"It's the wind that helps the old man's beard," he said, "and it's the wind that helps the dandelion and the thistle, isn't it?"

"Yes. Janet ought to have told me that," said Uncle Merry. "She forgot."

"Oh, Uncle, it's the birds that help the hips and haws," said Pat hurriedly. "They eat the nice fleshy skin-part and spit out the little stone inside the haw, and the hairy seeds inside the hip. I've seen them."

"Good boy!" said Uncle Merry, making a mark in his notebook.

The game went on. It was really exciting. It sent the children into fields and hedges; it made them examine big and small plants; it took them into every sort of green corner and nook. It was fun.

Then Janet brought some wild pansy seeds. "Look," she said, "the seed-cases press their edges together and

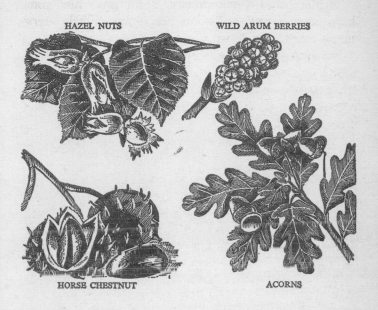

HAZEL NUTS

WILD ARUM BERRIES

HORSE CHESTNUT

ACORNS

shoot out the tiny seeds, Uncle, and they go springing high into the air."

"Quite right," said Uncle Merry. "A good many plants use the method of explosion to send out their seeds. Ah, John has brought one of our most interesting seed-heads?"

They all looked at the poppy-head, brown and hard, that John had found. "I can't quite see how the seeds come out," he said. "When I shake the poppy-head, Uncle, the seeds come out from somewhere, like a pepper-pot—look, little and black. Where do they come from?"

"Look under the ridge at the top of the head," said Uncle Merry. "There are some little holes or windows there. They don't open till the seeds are ripe. That's where they come out."

"Now, that really is clever," said John. "I suppose when the wind shakes the poppy-head it makes the seeds come bouncing out of the windows. Do I get a good mark for that, Uncle?"

"Half a mark," said Uncle Merry. "I had to give you some help!"

Pods of vetches were brought. Some of them twisted themselves round tightly, and shot their seeds out in that way. Capsules of foxglove were found, full of tiny black seed. Little goose-grass balls were brought by all three, and everyone knew that they were spread by passers-by. Even Fergus brought some of them on his coat.

John brought some seed-heads of the Umbrella Family. "I think these are the seed heads of the cow-parsley," said the little boy. "I brushed against them just now in the hedge, Uncle, and the plant catapulted its seeds all over me! Look—when I touch the seed-heads, some of the seeds shoot out at once."

"Good boy," said Uncle Merry. "The Umbrella Family likes to catapult its seeds away. They some-times shoot quite a good distance off. You see, it wouldn't do for seeds to fall just below their mother-plant, for then they would all grow up in the same place and choke one another. They must be sent a distance away by some means or other."

The children found a great many winged seeds flying from the trees. The sycamore sent its seeds away, flying on papery wings on the wind, and so did the maple. The elm gave each of its seeds one wing, and so did the pine. The birch filled the air with winged seeds too, escaping from the decaying catkins. It was amazing how many different kinds of seeds there were, and how many different ways the plants used to send them off on their journeys.

"Birds and animals help them, the wind helps them, and explosion helps them," said Janet. "Some seeds have fluff, some have wings, some have parachutes—it's simply marvellous!"

"White bryony berries, and black bryony berries," said John proudly, putting sprays into Uncle Merry's hands, "and honeysuckle berries, Uncle. They look good enough to eat!"

"Well, don't try," said Uncle Merry. "They are very poisonous! Hallo—Janet has brought what I was hoping someone would bring soon—a spike of wild arum berries."

The children looked at the erect spike of bright berries that Janet showed them. They remembered the curious cowl-like sheath of the wild arum or lords and ladies that they had seen in the spring-time, and the strange way in which the flower had made certain of being pollinated. They remembered the poker-like tongue. Now here was the arum again, showing its harvest, the brilliant spike of berries.

"It's nice to see the beginning and end of things," said Janet. "I like knowing the whole story."

105

"What with hooks and wings, parachutes and fluff, the babies of the plant world are very well provided for," said Pat. "Uncle, what a wonderful time of year this is for hunting for fruits and seeds, isn't it? I had simply no idea how full the fields and hedges and woods were of all these interesting things. It was fun finding the flowers in the spring and the summer—and it is even more fun now, finding the fruits and seeds that belong to them, and discovering how they send them out into the world."

"I think we'll stop the competition now," said Uncle Merry.

"Who has won the competition?" asked Pat.

"Count up your entries and tell me how many you have," said Uncle Merry. "Then I will add up the marks I have given you for knowledge or for common sense, and to-morrow I will tell you who has won."

"Why not to-day?" asked Pat, in disappointment.

"I have a reason," said Uncle Merry, and they had to be content with that.

They had taken a long time to find and bring their seeds and berries to Uncle Merry, and now they were all very hungry for their dinners. They turned to go home, thinking that they had had a really lovely morning.

As they went over the fields, John saw a strange bird feeding on berries in the hedgerow. "Look, Uncle," he said, "there's a bird I haven't seen before. How queer—I thought I knew all our common birds now."

"Ah—that's a migrant who has come down from the north to *us*," said Uncle Merry. "Some birds leave us and go south, John, and others come to us from the north. That is a fieldfare, one of the Thrush Family; and if you look hard over there, in the field, you will see another migrant who has arrived this month—the redwing."

"He belongs to the Thrush Family too, doesn't he?" said John. "Oh, now he is flying, and I can see why he is called the redwing—his wings show chestnut-red when he flies, Uncle."

"Right," said Uncle Merry. "You will see both the fieldfare and redwing flocking together with the thrushes in the winter fields, John, and you will easily be able to tell that they all belong to the Thrush Family, for they have the same freckled breasts. You must watch carefully, and see if you can tell one from the other."

"It will be November soon," said Pat gloomily. "No walks then, I suppose, Uncle, because there will be nothing much to see."

"Well, I was hoping you would all come for walks with me till the end of the year," said Uncle Merry; "but, of course, if you really think there will be nothing to see, please don't come, Pat."

"Of course I shall come!" said Pat hastily. "I might know there would always be plenty to see if *you* took us out, Uncle. Goodness me, I believe you'd see plenty if you went out in the middle of a winter's night in a thick snowstorm!"

That made everyone laugh. They said good-bye at their gates, and went in. The children's mother was amazed to see all the things they had brought back with them.

"Who won?" she asked; but nobody knew. They

didn't know till the next day, when a little note arrived from Uncle Merry, and a large parcel.

"You all did so well that I can't put anyone top or bottom," he wrote. "I am sending you prizes for being so clever. The bird-book is for John. The flower-book is for Janet. The animal-book is for Pat."

"Oh, isn't he kind?" cried Janet, opening her flower-book. "Look—there are coloured pictures of every single one of our wild flowers—just exactly what I wanted! And, John—look—there are coloured pictures of all our wild birds for you—and of all our wild creatures for Pat! Let's rush in to Uncle Merry, and give him a big hug!"

They did—and he was very pleased. "You deserve your prizes," he said; "and I hope you'll use them well, year after year!"

CHAPTER 11

GREEN TREES IN NOVEMBER

IN the last week of November the mists suddenly cleared, and the sun shone down, pale, but very welcome. The sky was cloudless, and the children ran to find Uncle Merry.

"I thought you would be in to-day to drag me out for a walk," he said, with a laugh. "You thought so too, didn't you, Fergus?"

"Wuff," said the Scottie eagerly.

"I saw the thrushes pulling at the rose-hips to-day,"

said John, as they all went down the lane, Fergus running in front; "and a tit came and swung on the bone I hung at my window, Uncle. The robin that lives in our garden came and sat on my window-sill yesterday, too. The birds seem to be getting very tame now."

"We'll put up a bird-table next month," said Uncle Merry. "That's a good way to bring our common birds close enough for us to see them and recognise them."

"Oh, that would be fine," said Pat, pleased. "I've always wanted a bird-table."

"Now—look out for evergreens," said Uncle Merry. "Who will see the first?"

"I will!" shouted all three children at once, and each of them pointed at the privet hedge that ran round a cottage garden in the lane.

"Right," said Uncle Merry. "Now look out for the next. It's really easy in winter-time, when no other tree is clothed in leaves."

"Don't the evergreens ever grow new leaves?" asked Pat. "Do they keep their old ones on year after year?"

"Oh, evergreens shed their leaves, of course," said Uncle Merry; "but they don't shed them all at once, in a few weeks, as the other trees do. They drop them little by little all the year round. Haven't you noticed the pine-needles under the pine tree, old and brown on the ground? And have you never seen the withered privet leaves lying on the ground under your privet hedge?"

"Oh yes, of course," said Pat, remembering. "Uncle, is it a good idea to keep leaves on all the winter through? It does save a lot of bother, doesn't it?"

"Well, I suppose it does," said Uncle Merry, laughing. "But you must remember that it is not so good for evergreen trees when the snow comes. Their big, leaf-spread branches hold the snow, and very often the great weight of the snow breaks their branches right off. But the snow slips easily off the bare boughs of the other trees, such as oak or elm, and they do not mind it at all."

"Evergreen, Uncle," said John, pointing to a prickly holly tree. "Look at the berries forming. We shall be able to get some good holly this year for Christmas decoration."

"Yes, the holly is evergreen," said Uncle. "Hurry up and find some more. There is plenty about."

"There's one!" said Janet, pointing to a tall straight-trunked tree. "It's a Christmas tree, Uncle."

"So it is," said Uncle Merry. "What's its proper name?"

No one knew. "Spruce fir," said Uncle Merry. "You can always tell it by the spire at the top—do you see it?"

The children looked up and saw the short, spiky spire sticking straight up at the top of the tree. They also saw long cones hanging downwards from some of the branches.

"Cones!" said Janet. "I like them. Here's one on the ground, Uncle. Are the seeds held behind these woody scales?"

"Yes," said Uncle Merry. "They are winged, of course. The spruce fir flowers in May. You must look next May for the flowers at the end of this year's shoots."

"This spruce fir is a very big Christmas tree," said John. "I wish we could have one like this for Christmas, instead of a little one. How lovely it would look all covered with toys and ornaments, and lighted with candles!"

"It certainly would!" agreed Uncle Merry. "Come along—next evergreen, please!"

"I can see an evergreen, but it isn't a tree," said Janet, and she pointed to where the ivy was still flowering on a sheltered hedge. "The ivy keeps green all the winter through, doesn't it, Uncle?"

"It does," said her uncle. "Good—that's another evergreen. Who will find the next?"

"There's one," said Pat, as they came towards a big green tree. "It must be a fir, Uncle, but it's not a spruce fir, because it hasn't the sharp spire at the top."

"Its leaves are rather the same," said Janet, feeling the short, needle-like leaves. "What funny leaves the firs have, Uncle—not broad and flat like those of ordinary trees."

"This is a silver fir," said Uncle Merry. He pointed to the trunk. "This is an old tree," he said. "Do you see the silvery grey trunk? It must be two or three hundred years old."

"Gracious," said Janet, startled. "Uncle, do silver firs really grow to that age?"

"Oh, they grow to four hundred years," said Uncle Merry. "Trees are among our longest-lived things, Janet. Oak trees live for many centuries—more than you would believe!"

"The top of this silver fir is flattish, not spired," said Pat, looking up. "And, Uncle, there's a smaller silver fir over there, with a bushy top. That's an easy way of telling whether it's a spruce or a silver fir, isn't it?"

They left the old silver fir behind them and went towards the pine woods. "Heaps of evergreens here," said John. "I like pine trees, Uncle. Oh, there's the grey squirrel! He must have wakened up to-day. Fergus, silly dog—what's the use of chasing a squirrel? You can't climb trees after him!"

Fergus stood with his front paws on the trunk of the tree up which the squirrel had gone, and he whined loudly.

"He's telling Uncle Merry that it's an evergreen," said Janet, with a chuckle. "He says, with a whine, 'I'm sure it's a pine!'"

"Idiot!" said Pat. Everyone laughed. They looked at the big pine tree. "It has needle-like leaves, too," said Pat, "but longer than those on the firs. And, Uncle, look at the cones—they are smaller, and egg-shaped. I suppose they have winged seeds tucked away safely beneath the scales?"

"Yes," said Uncle Merry. "This tree is the Scotch pine. Do you see how its lower branches have withered, and look old and broken? Most pines look like that."

They went through the pine wood, looking out for the grey squirrel, but he didn't appear again. They came out into the fields, and John pointed to a tall tree growing by the lane-side there. "A yew!" he said. "That's an evergreen, isn't it, Uncle? Look—it's still covered with the waxen-red berries, and there is a thrush busy eating them."

"The birds are very fond of yew berries," said Uncle Merry. "We must look for the flowers early in the spring-time. If we strike the branches of a yew bush then, we shall see a great cloud of yellow pollen fly out."

"Isn't the trunk of the yew queer?" said John, looking at the reddish bole. "Uncle, it looks as if several trunks have all grown together, doesn't it?"

"It does," said his uncle, looking at the stout and rugged trunk. "That is typical of yews. It used to be a very important tree in the old days, John, because our long-bows were made of yew, and they were the chief weapons of our old-time soldiers."

"It has needle-like leaves like the other trees we have seen," said Janet, feeling them. "Uncle, why are the leaves this shape, instead of being broad and flat?"

"Plants give off moisture through their leaves," said Uncle Merry. "They do not want to do this in wintertime, because they need all their moisture—so they grow thin, narrow leaves, with very little surface, which means that they cannot give off much moisture. Sometimes they have a tough surface to their leaves too, as in the holly—this also means that they cannot give off moisture easily. Any plants that live on windswept places, such as heaths and moors, grow these narrow leaves. Can you think of plants that do that?"

"Yes—the heather," said John, at once.

"Right," said Uncle Merry, "and what about the gorse, with its narrow, spiny leaves?"

"Oh yes!" said the children, remembering the curious gorse bushes, with only sharp spines for leaves.

Uncle Merry pointed out a big tree standing at the end of a field, its great flat branches spreading out horizontally from the trunk. "Do you know what that is?" he asked. The children shook their heads.

"A cedar," said Uncle Merry. "It's the only one in

113

this district. You can always tell a cedar by its curious flat-spreading branches."

"The cedar tree comes into the Bible," said Pat. "It's called the cedar of Lebanon there. So that's a cedar, is it? I always wondered what it was like."

They turned to go home, for it was getting late. "There don't seem to be any more evergreens to be seen," said Janet. "Are there, Uncle?"

"Well, there are two in the garden at home—no, three," said Uncle Merry. "We'll have a look round when we get there."

"Uncle—look at Fergus—he's chasing a rabbit round that tree!" suddenly cried Pat. They all stopped to look.

A large sandy-brown rabbit was running round and round a big oak tree. Fergus was tearing after it, uttering short yelps of excitement. He had never been so near a rabbit before!

The rabbit scampered round and round the oak tree merrily, its white tail bobbing. John stared with wide eyes. Then he clutched Uncle Merry's arm.

"Uncle! Fergus isn't chasing the rabbit—the rabbit is chasing Fergus! Oh, Uncle, really the rabbit is chasing Fergus!"

The rabbit suddenly popped under a gorse bush and disappeared. Fergus still went on round and round the tree, for he had had the trunk between him and the rabbit, and he had not seen its disappearance. After a few moments he stopped in surprise. Where was that rabbit?

He sniffed about a little and then came towards the laughing children, his tail drooping.

114

"Fergus! That rabbit was chasing *you!*" said John. "No wonder you've got your tail down!"

"John, you really mustn't insult Fergus by saying such a thing!" said Uncle Merry, with a twinkle. "No Scottie would ever admit that anything could chase him. You nearly caught the rabbit, didn't you, Fergus?"

"Wuff," said Fergus, wagging his tail again, and looking happier.

"He says of course he was chasing it!" said Janet.

So, that point being settled, the five of them turned homewards. They collected a few flowers on the way, but not so many as in the walk before. They saw the birds in big flocks. They found some strange toad-stools, and some fungi growing out of a rotten tree-trunk. They even saw a moth at rest on a tree. Uncle Merry said it was the November moth.

"Queer that it should choose this month to come out in," said Janet, surprised.

They reached home, and went into the garden to find the three evergreens that Uncle Merry said were there. John spotted one at once.

"The laurel," he said, pointing to the leathery green leaves of the big bushes.

"And the rhododendron!" said John. "Now, Janet, you find the third one."

But Janet couldn't, and nor could John or Pat. So Uncle Merry had to point it out to them.

"There it is," he said, pointing to the little box-edging that ran round the kitchen garden. "Box is an evergreen. Look at its green leaves. It's only an edging here, but you will find it as a bush or as a tall tree in other places, holding on to its green leaves all the winter through."

"All three of these garden evergreens have tough, leathery leaves," said John, feeling them. "Is that to prevent them from losing too much moisture, Uncle?"

"Yes," said Uncle Merry. "Quite right, John. And now, come along, Fergus, we must get indoors and do some work. Good-bye. children. We'll go for a walk before Christmas, shall we? And don't let's forget about the bird-table!"

"No, we won't!" said the children. "Good-bye, Uncle. See you soon!"

CHAPTER 12

CHRISTMAS DAY

"It's December," said Janet, looking at the calendar. "Soon it will be Christmas!"

"Oooh—lovely!" said John, thinking of Christmas stockings, Christmas trees, and Christmas pudding.

"It's really winter now," said Pat, looking out of the window. "Not even Uncle Merry would find very much that is exciting."

"We have been for walks every month this year," said John. "I've loved them. I've learnt such a lot too —things I never knew before."

"And I've got a lot of lovely pictures stored up in my mind," said Janet. "Do you remember the golden buttercup fields, John?"

"Yes—I remember," said John. "And I remember the blue kingfisher diving into the stream, and the lovely swallows soaring through the air."

"And I remember old Fergus being chased by a rabbit last month," chuckled Pat. But Janet and John flew to Fergus's defence at once.

"The rabbit was *not* chasing him. They were going round and round that oak tree, but Fergus was after the rabbit, you know he was, Pat!"

"I should just think so!" said Uncle Merry's voice, and he walked into the room with Fergus at his heels. I've got to go away for a while before Christmas, so perhaps our next walk could be on Christmas Day itself."

"Oh, Uncle Merry, that would be lovely!" said Janet. "Uncle Merry, Mother says will you come to Christmas dinner with us? We'd love to have you."

"Thank you," said Uncle Merry. "I accept with pleasure—but is Fergus also invited?"

"Of *course*!" said John, kneeling down by the Scottie, and giving him a hug. "As a matter of fact, Uncle Merry, we wanted *Fergus* here for Christmas, and as we couldn't get him without you, we just *had* to ask you too!" John had such a wicked twinkle in his eye as he spoke that Uncle Merry chased him all round the nursery.

"Now, now, children," said Mother, appearing at the door. "Really, Mr. Meredith, you are as bad as the children!"

Before Christmas the children went out together, and cut down holly boughs, scarlet with berries, and a big tuft of mistletoe from the oak tree. They carried

117

them home, looking like children on a Christmas card, with the holly over their shoulders.

They decorated Uncle Merry's study and it looked so gay and Christmassy. Each of the children had brought a present for him. They wrapped up the presents in gay paper, wrote loving messages, and left them on Uncle Merry's table. He was not coming back till Christmas Eve.

"I hope he'll like the new walking stick I bought," said Pat. "I chose it very carefully. It's got a nice crooky handle for dragging down catkin branches and things like that."

"I've embroidered M for Merry on a big white hanky as nicely as ever I could," said Janet.

"You needn't tell us that again," said Pat. "We've seen you doing it for at least three weeks!"

"I don't think much of my present for him, really," said John, thinking that the others had bought Uncle Merry very nice presents indeed. "I've only got this new notebook for him and a *very* sharp pencil. It's to put down his notes about birds. I saw that his notebook was old and almost full."

"He'll like the painting of a bird you've made on the cover," said Janet.

It was dark when the children got back to their own house. Their mother met them, looking quite sad.

"Children, the Christmas tree hasn't come! You know, the one they sent was too small, so I sent it back—and the greengrocer promised to send another. Now I hear that he hasn't any left at all."

This was sad news indeed. No Christmas tree!

"Never mind," said Janet. "We'll get one after Christmas, and dress it then."

Christmas morning dawned brilliantly. The boys couldn't think why their bedroom was so full of dazzling white light. But Janet soon told them!

"It's snowed in the night! Oh, come and look, Pat and John! Everywhere is buried in thick white snow!"

The countryside was beautiful in its white mantle. The garden was very still. Everything was softened by the dazzling snow. The children were thrilled.

"Just exactly right for Christmas Day!" they said, and rushed to see what was in their stockings. They made such a noise that their mother came to enjoy the fun.

"Uncle Merry came in last night after you had gone to bed," said Mother. "He is back again. He was sad to hear that we hadn't a Christmas tree. He is coming in after breakfast with a present for you all."

"Oh, how lovely!" said Janet. "Oh, Mother, where did I put my present for Fergus? It's a most wonderful collar, with a plaid pattern all round it—just right for a Scottie dog!"

She soon found it. John found his present for Fergus too—an enormous bone. Pat had a drinking bowl for him with DOG on it. "Now the cat will know it isn't hers," said John, when he saw it. That made the others laugh.

Uncle Merry came staggering into the garden after breakfast, carrying such a heavy load! Over one shoulder was a perfectly lovely Christmas tree, and over the other a funny thing with one stout leg.

"Happy Christmas, happy Christmas!" shouted everyone, and Fergus wuffed exactly as if he were saying "Happy Christmas" too!

"I went out and dug up a nice little Christmas tree

for you out of my garden this morning," said Uncle Merry, panting. "It *was* hard work—but I couldn't bear to think of three nice children like you without any Christmas tree on Christmas Day!"

"Oh, *thank* you, Uncle Merry!" cried the children. "It's a beauty! We'll plant it back in your garden again when we've finished with it."

The spruce fir was put into a big tub, and stood in the hall, ready to be decorated. Then Uncle Merry took the children out into the garden to see the present he had made for them.

"It's between you all," he said, "and I hope it will give you much pleasure for years to come. It's the bird-table I promised you!"

"Oh, how lovely!" said Janet, looking at the strong table with its one tall leg. "Uncle, it's so nice and big. Oh, I'm longing to see some birds on it!"

They dug a hole for the leg, and Uncle Merry rammed it in. Then the table was firm, and was just too high for the cat to jump up on it. Fergus whined and tried to stand up against the pole, but he was far too short to see on the table. He was wearing his new collar, and was very proud of it. He had had a drink out of his new bowl, and a nibble at his bone, so he was very happy. He had had a good look at the letters D-O-G on his bowl, and John felt certain he knew what the word said!

Uncle Merry was delighted with his lovely presents. He wore Janet's hanky in his breast pocket, and he put John's notebook into his inside pocket straight away. "Just what I want," he said, "and as for Pat's stick, I shall have to take it out this afternoon."

They nailed twigs at the back of the bird-table, and

bound sprays of hips and haws tightly to them. They spread the table with other berries, and seeds that Uncle Merry had either bought or collected.

"We'll buy some pea-nuts for the tits, and string them on a thread, through their shells," said Uncle Merry. "And I wonder if we could spare one or two potatoes cooked in their jackets. The birds love those."

Soon the table was spread with food of all kinds. No birds flew down to it, though, much to the children's disappointment. They sat at the window, munching bars of chocolate, which Fergus had given to them for Christmas.

Janet suddenly gave a little squeal. "Uncle Merry! There's a sparrow! I'm sure he's going to fly down to the table!"

The inquisitive little brown bird was sitting on a nearby twig, looking at the spread table with his head cocked knowingly on one side. What was this? He would fly down and see.

He flew down on to the table, and began to peck at the boiled potato. Then another sparrow flew down and yet another.

The robin flew down to the twigs nailed behind the table, and watched for a chance to hop down, take a beakful of food and hop back again. He didn't like feeding with the noisy sparrows.

Then a big freckled thrush came, and the blackbird. They pecked greedily at the potato, and ran at the sparrows to frighten them away.

A chaffinch came, and then a blue-tit. The watching children were really thrilled.

"Oh, Uncle Merry," said John, "this is a grand present you've given us! We shall simply love watching the table day after day."

"You must put a bowl of water on the table too," said Uncle Merry. "The birds suffer a good deal from thirst in the winter-time. The water will freeze up, of course, but you can renew it each morning, and the birds will soon learn to come and take a sip when you have put it out."

Christmas dinner was fun. The turkey was enormous, and the Christmas pudding was set alight so that it flamed brightly when it was carried in. Everyone was glad to have Uncle Merry there, and as for Fergus, he had the time of his life. He sat close by John's legs under the table and eagerly ate all the tit-bits that John passed down to him.

After dinner they put on hats and coats and went for a walk. First they hunted under the snow for the Christmas roses, and found five of them out, hiding under the white blanket. It was sweet to see them there. John ran indoors to give them to his mother.

"Uncle Merry, how does the mistletoe grow on the oak, and on the other trees? How does it get there, to begin with?" asked Pat.

"The missel-thrush put it there," said Uncle Merry, smiling to see the astonished faces of the three children. "That's why he is called missel-thrush, because he is so fond of mistletoe berries."

"How does he plant them?" asked John.

"Well, the mistletoe berries are very sticky," said Uncle Merry. "The thrush has a good feast of them, and then he wants to clean his beak. So he wipes his bill carefully on a bough, leaving behind him one or two of the sticky mistletoe seeds. These put out what are called 'sinkers'—suckers that pierce through the bark of the tree right down into the sap."

"And then the mistletoe draws up the sap and lives on it!" said Janet. "Very cunning!"

"Very," said Uncle Merry. "As soon as it has several sinkers drawing up sap, it grows a pair of sage-green leaves. The mistletoe's leaves are never the rich tender green of ordinary plants, as I expect you have

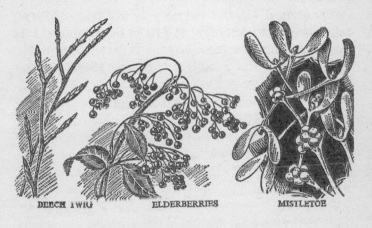

BEECH TWIG   ELDERBERRIES   MISTLETOE

noticed. It has the dull colouring that many parasites show."

"It gets others to do its work," said John. "I don't think it's a very good plant. If I were a plant, I would do my own work, and not live on others."

"Quite right!" said Uncle Merry. "'I hope you will always feel like that."

"We really and truly shan't see any flowers in the countryside to-day," said Pat, as they trudged down the snowy lane. "I doubt if we shall see anything, shall we,

123

Uncle Merry, except a few birds? Surely no animal will be out to-day!"

But although they saw no animal at all, not even a rabbit, they saw where many creatures had been. The snow showed their footprints very clearly indeed. It was John who noticed them first.

"Look!" he said, "are these a rabbit's prints, Uncle? There are some round marks for his front-paws, and some longer ones where his strong hind-legs touched the snow."

"Yes," said Uncle Merry, "you will find plenty of rabbit footprints about here. The bunnies will come to gnaw the bark of these ivy-stems if the snow stays for long, because the grass they usually nibble will be hidden."

By the pond the children found marks of webbed feet in the snow. "Ducks," said Janet, at once. "And look, Uncle, you can easily see which footprints are made by hopping birds or walking birds, can't you?"

"How can you tell?" asked Pat, looking at them.

"Because hopping birds put their feet side by side, and walking birds put them one after the other as we do," said Janet. "I should have thought you would have guessed that, silly!"

They examined all the footprints they came to, and it was really very exciting. They saw where the pheasants had roosted, and left the marks of their tails. They discovered where a stoat had chased a frightened rabbit, his neat, round little marks mingled with the prints of the scampering bunny.

"What's this? Is it a dog or a cat?" asked Janet, pointing to a line of foot-prints on the snowy hillside. Uncle Merry shook his head.

"Not a cat, because she draws in her claws when she walks, and you can see the claw-marks in these clear snow-prints," he said. "Not a dog, because you can see here and there where a tail has brushed the snow—a big tail too!"

The children stared at the prints. John suddenly guessed the owner of the marks. "A fox, of course," he said. "Isn't it, Uncle? A fox! He stood here on the hillside watching the rabbits at play, his tail brushing the snow behind him. Uncle Merry, there's quite a story in some of these footprints!"

"There is," agreed Uncle Merry. "Hallo, Fergus! Did you think it was time to go home? Poor old fellow, your short legs soon get tired, floundering over the snow, don't they?"

"He makes wonderful snow-prints," said John. "Look—quite deep ones—and he shows his claws in them nicely. All right, Fergus, we'll go home to tea."

Fergus was glad. He was not built for walking in the snow. He found it very difficult to wade along, for he sank almost to his body in the snow. He turned to go home, wagging his tail hard. He wanted to get back to that beautiful bone that John had given him!

"I can see now how the evergreen trees hold the snow," said Janet, as they went home. "Look at that silver fir, Uncle—one of its boughs is almost breaking."

"The other trees, which have lost their leaves, have hardly any snow on at all," said Pat. "It has slipped off."

They soon reached home, shook the snow off their boots, and went indoors. The first thing they saw was the Christmas tree that Uncle Merry had brought for them. It was in the hall, and Mother had decorated it whilst they had been out. It was simply beautiful!

Christmas Day came to an end at last. The children hugged Uncle Merry when he said good-night.

"We've had such a happy year," said Janet, "all because of you, Uncle Merry. We've learnt to know and love a thousand different things; and now we've begun, we shall go on."

"Yes," said John shyly, "the biggest present you've given us is the key of the countryside, Uncle!"

"A very sweet thing to say!" said Uncle Merry, giving the little boy a hug. "Well, there's one thing about *that* key, John—once you've got it, you never, never lose it! Good night!"

"Wuff!" said Fergus, following his master out into the darkness of the front garden.

"He says 'Good night and happy dreams,'" said Janet. "Same to you, Fergus. Good night, Uncle Merry, good night!"

There are three other Nature books as well !

Nature Lover's Book Number 1
Nature Lover's Book Number 3
Nature Lover's Book Number 4

Price 17½p each